# GCSE English
# Much Ado About Nothing

## by William Shakespeare

We have a confession — this CGP *Much Ado About Nothing* Workbook
isn't *quite* as funny as Shakespeare's rip-roaring Sicilian comedy.
But it'll still have you laughing all the way to exam success...

It's packed with practice questions to build up your understanding of the play —
plot, characters, themes, Shakespeare's techniques and more. There's even
an Exam Buster section that'll have you writing brilliant essays in no time.

So true love isn't always as complicated as *Much Ado* would have you believe.
You and this Workbook were meant to be together ♥

# The Workbook

# CONTENTS

# Contents

Published by CGP

*Editors:*
Claire Boulter
Tom Carney
Andy Cashmore
Eleanor Claringbold
Emma Cleasby
Sophie Herring
Matt Topping

With thanks to Jack Tooth and Nicola Woodfin for the proofreading.
With thanks to Ana Pungartnik for the copyright research.

*Acknowledgements:*

With thanks to Geraint Lewis for permission to use the front cover image.

With thanks to Rex Features for permission to use the images on pages 1, 35, 44 & 46.

With thanks to Photostage for permission to use the images on pages 2, 4, 7, 8, 10, 12, 20, 23, 24, 25, 26, 29, 30, 32 & 41.

With thanks to Alamy for permission to use the images on pages 15, 18 & 22.

With thanks to ArenaPAL for permission to use the images on pages 19, 21, 36, 39 & 42.

ISBN: 978 1 78908 143 5

Printed by Elanders Ltd, Newcastle upon Tyne.

Clipart from Corel®

# How to Use this Book

## Practise the four main skills you'll need for the exam

Each question tests <u>one or more</u> of the <u>four skills</u> you'll be tested on in the <u>exam</u>. You'll need to:

1) Write about the text in a <u>thoughtful way</u>, <u>picking out</u> appropriate <u>examples</u> and <u>quotations</u> to back up your opinions.

2) <u>Identify</u> and <u>explain</u> features of the play's <u>form</u>, <u>structure</u> and <u>language</u>. Using <u>subject terminology</u>, show how the author uses these to create <u>characters</u> and <u>settings</u>, explore <u>themes</u> and affect the <u>audience's reactions</u>.

3) Write about the play's <u>context</u> in your exam.

4) Write in a <u>clear</u>, <u>well-structured</u> and <u>accurate</u> way. <u>5%</u> of the marks in your English Literature GCSE are for <u>spelling</u>, <u>punctuation</u> and <u>grammar</u>.

Most exam boards will want you write about context. Ask your teacher if you're not sure.

## You can use this workbook with the CGP Text Guide

1) This book is perfect to use with CGP's <u>Text Guide</u> for *Much Ado About Nothing*. It matches each <u>main section</u> of the Text Guide, so you can test your understanding of the play <u>bit by bit</u>.

2) The workbook tests all the <u>important</u> parts of the text that you'll need to know about for the exam — <u>plot</u>, <u>characters</u>, <u>context</u>, <u>themes</u> and <u>Shakespeare's techniques</u>.

3) The questions refer to the text <u>in detail</u> — you'll need a <u>copy</u> of the play to make the most of the workbook. The line numbers used throughout this book match CGP's <u>Much Ado About Nothing — The Complete Play</u>.

© Sam Goldwyn/Renaissance/BBC/Kobal/REX/Shutterstock

## It prepares you for the exam every step of the way

1) The exam section is jam-packed with <u>useful advice</u>. It <u>guides</u> you through how to tackle the exam, from understanding the questions to building great answers. There's also an easy-to-read <u>mark scheme</u>, which you can use to mark <u>sample answers</u> and improve answers of your <u>own</u>.

2) There are four pages of <u>practice exam questions</u> spread across the book. They give you the opportunity to use what you've revised in each section to write a <u>realistic answer</u>.

3) <u>Exam tips</u> and extra <u>practice exam questions</u> are included throughout the book. There are also helpful <u>revision tasks</u> designed to get you thinking more creatively. These are marked with <u>stamps</u>.

4) You can find <u>answers</u> to all of the <u>questions</u> and <u>tasks</u> at the back of the book.

5) Each section contains at least one 'Skills Focus' page. These pages help you to practise important skills <u>individually</u>. You can tackle them in <u>any order</u> and prioritise the skills you find the <u>hardest</u>.

## *We should have called this book Much To Do With Revision...*

Now you're clued up on what this lovely book has to offer, it's time to leap head first into some questions. You're not in the exam just yet, so don't panic — just take your time and go through the book at your own pace.

# Section One — Analysis of Acts

## Act One

### Act 1, Scene 1 — Claudio falls in love with Hero

**Q1** Put these events in order by numbering the boxes. The first one has been done for you.

Don Pedro and his men arrive at Leonato's house. ☐

Beatrice and Benedick argue with each other. ☐

Leonato learns that Don Pedro is coming to Messina. 1

Don Pedro decides to stay with Leonato for a month. ☐

The Messenger reveals that Claudio has gained glory in the war. ☐

Beatrice asks if Benedick has returned from the war. ☐

Benedick says that he isn't capable of loving anyone. ☐

**Q2** Identify who said each of these phrases, then explain what each one means.

**a) "I see, lady, the gentleman is not in your books."**     Said by: ..........................................

Meaning: ...............................................................................................................................

**b) "But it is certain I am loved of all ladies"**     Said by: ..........................................

Meaning: ...............................................................................................................................

**Q3** Read lines 151-241. Find a quote to back up each of these statements.

**a)** Claudio thinks that Hero is attractive.

...............................................................................................................................

**b)** Benedick is confident that he will never marry.

...............................................................................................................................

**Q4** Read lines 272-310. What impression does the audience get of Don Pedro in this passage? Support your answer with a quote.

...............................................................................................................................

...............................................................................................................................

...............................................................................................................................

...............................................................................................................................

© Donald Cooper/photostage

## Act 1, Scene 2 — Antonio tells Leonato that Don Pedro loves Hero

**Q1**  Decide whether each statement is **true** or **false**, and find a quote to back up your answer.

**a)**  Antonio thinks that Leonato won't be surprised by the rumour.     **True:** ☐  **False:** ☐

Quote: ........................................................................................................

........................................................................................................

**b)**  Leonato is cautious about believing Antonio's news.     **True:** ☐  **False:** ☐

Quote: ........................................................................................................

........................................................................................................

**Q2**  What does Leonato plan to do after hearing the rumour?

........................................................................................................

## Act 1, Scene 3 — Don John plans to ruin Claudio and Hero's wedding

**Q3**  Why does Conrade suggest that Don John should hide his dissatisfaction?

........................................................................................................

**Q4**  Don John claims he would rather be "**disdained of all than to fashion a carriage to rob love from any**".  State what this quote means, then explain what it suggests about Don John.

Meaning: ........................................................................................................

Explanation: ........................................................................................................

........................................................................................................

**Q5**  Why do you think Don John is interested in ruining the potential marriage between Claudio and Hero?  Explain your answer.

........................................................................................................

........................................................................................................

### *You Don want to get your Johns and Pedros mixed up...*

Shakespeare uses Act 1 to set up all of the play's main romantic relationships, friendships and family relationships.  As you're reading the play, have a think about how these relationships change and why.

 ☐   ☐   ☐

4

# Act Two

## Act 2, Scene 1 — Don Pedro woos Hero for Claudio

**Q1** Find a quote from this scene to support each of the following statements.

**a)** Beatrice doesn't want to be obedient to a husband.

.......................................................................................................................

**b)** Leonato wants Hero to marry Don Pedro if he asks.

.......................................................................................................................

**c)** Beatrice is confident that Hero will attract attention at the ball.

.......................................................................................................................

**Q2** Decide whether these statements about the masked ball are **true** or **false**.

|  | True | False |
|---|---|---|
| Don Pedro woos Hero for himself. | ☐ | ☐ |
| Don Pedro is disguised when he woos Hero. | ☐ | ☐ |
| Hero is nervous around Don Pedro. | ☐ | ☐ |
| Don John tries to cause trouble for Claudio. | ☐ | ☐ |
| Claudio becomes jealous of Don Pedro. | ☐ | ☐ |
| Leonato doesn't want Claudio to marry Hero. | ☐ | ☐ |

**Q3** Read lines 109-146. How does Shakespeare suggest in this passage that women are observant? Give two ways.

1) .................................................................................................................

2) .................................................................................................................

**Q4** Read lines 204-228. Why doesn't Benedick feel sympathy for Claudio? Explain your answer.

.......................................................................................................................

.......................................................................................................................

.......................................................................................................................

## Act 2, Scene 1 continued — Don John's plan fails

**Q1** Read lines 232-255. In this passage, how does Benedick react to Beatrice's insults? Find a quote to support your answer.

.......................................................................................................................................

.......................................................................................................................................

Quote: ...............................................................................................................................

**Q2** Read lines 270-280. Find a quote that suggests Beatrice has been hurt by Benedick in the past. Explain how this might affect the audience's impression of Beatrice.

Quote: ...............................................................................................................................

Explanation: .......................................................................................................................

.......................................................................................................................................

**Q3** Why does Don John's plan to break up Claudio and Hero fail?

.......................................................................................................................................

**Q4** Read lines 295-302. How does Claudio react when he is given permission to marry Hero?

.......................................................................................................................................

.......................................................................................................................................

## Act 2, Scene 2 — Borachio suggests a new plan to ruin Hero

**Q5** Why do you think Shakespeare reveals Borachio's plot at this point in the play? Explain your answer.

.......................................................................................................................................

.......................................................................................................................................

**Q6** Explain how Borachio plans to make Hero seem unfaithful. Use a quote to support your answer.

.......................................................................................................................................

.......................................................................................................................................

.......................................................................................................................................

## Act 2, Scene 3 — Don Pedro tricks Benedick

**Q1** Read lines 23-38. In Act 1, Benedick suggests that he will never marry. How does this passage reinforce Benedick's attitude from Act 1? Use a quote to support your answer.

.......................................................................................................................................................

.......................................................................................................................................................

.......................................................................................................................................................

**Q2** In this scene, Balthasar says "**many a wooer doth commence his suit / To her he thinks not worthy, yet he woos, / Yet will he swear he loves**". Explain what he is suggesting about men.

.......................................................................................................................................................

.......................................................................................................................................................

**Q3** Decide whether the following statements are **true** or **false**.
For each one, find a short quote to support your answer.

**a)** Claudio is confident that Benedick will fall for the trick.　　**True:** ☐　**False:** ☐

Quote: ...................................................................................

**b)** Benedick is disappointed when he thinks Beatrice loves him.　　**True:** ☐　**False:** ☐

Quote: ...................................................................................

**Q4** Read lines 212-218. In your own words, explain the next stage of Don Pedro's plan to get Benedick and Beatrice to fall in love.

.......................................................................................................................................................

.......................................................................................................................................................

**Q5** Read lines 247-263. Explain how Shakespeare uses Benedick and Beatrice in this passage to create humour.

.......................................................................................................................................................

.......................................................................................................................................................

.......................................................................................................................................................

### Don Pedro — the ultimate Shakespearean wingman...

The theme of deception is important throughout the play, but it plays an especially big role in Act 2. You should think about how the tricks and deception in this act help move the plot of the play along.

# Act Three

## Act 3, Scene 1 — Hero tricks Beatrice

**Q1** Read lines 1-25. Find a quote that makes Hero seem assertive. Explain how her behaviour has changed since Act 1.

Quote: ................................................................................................

................................................................................................

Explanation: ................................................................................................

................................................................................................

© Donald Cooper/photostage

**Q2** Beatrice comes to the orchard very soon after Margaret leaves to carry out Hero's plan. What does this suggest about Hero's relationship with Beatrice? Explain your answer.

................................................................................................

................................................................................................

**Q3** Fill in the table below to show the similarities between Act 2, Scene 3 and Act 3, Scene 1. The first one has been done for you.

| Example from Act 2, Scene 3 | How it is mirrored in Act 3, Scene 1 |
|---|---|
| **a)** Claudio refers to hunting to show that he and the others are laying a trap for Benedick. | Ursula refers to fishing to make her laying the trap for Beatrice seem like a sport. |
| **b)** Don Pedro claims Benedick has a "**contemptible spirit**" in his hearing. | |
| **c)** Don Pedro compliments Beatrice by calling her an "**excellent sweet lady**". | |
| **d)** Claudio claims Beatrice will die if Benedick does not love her back. | |

**Q4** Beatrice exclaims "**Contempt, farewell, and maiden pride, adieu!**" (line 109). Explain how this shows that her attitude towards love has changed since Act 1.

The word 'adieu' means 'goodbye' in French.

................................................................................................

................................................................................................

................................................................................................

................................................................................................

**Section One — Analysis of Acts**

## Act 3, Scene 2 — Don John tricks Claudio

**Q1** Benedick has shaved and is wearing perfume in this scene, which associates him with the courtly love tradition. Why is this significant at this point in the play? Explain your answer.

..................................................................................................................................................

..................................................................................................................................................

**Q2** Why do you think Claudio and Don Pedro mock Benedick for being in love? Explain your answer.

..................................................................................................................................................

..................................................................................................................................................

**Q3** Claudio decides that he will shame Hero publicly if he finds out that she is disloyal. How might this affect the audience's impression of him?

..................................................................................................................................................

..................................................................................................................................................

## Act 3, Scene 3 — The Watch arrest Borachio and Conrade

**Q4** How does Shakespeare make the Watch seem incompetent in this scene? Give two ways.

1) ...........................................................................................

...........................................................................................

2) ...........................................................................................

...........................................................................................

© Donald Cooper/photostage

**Q5** Read lines 141-161. According to Borachio, why did his plan to make Hero seem unfaithful work? Use a quote to support your answer.

..................................................................................................................................................

..................................................................................................................................................

..................................................................................................................................................

**Section One — Analysis of Acts**

## Act 3, Scene 4 — Hero gets ready for the wedding

**Q1**  How does Shakespeare emphasise Hero's innocence in this scene?  Explain your answer.

.................................................................................................................................................

.................................................................................................................................................

**Q2**  Read lines 39-67.  Explain how Beatrice feels in this passage.  Support your answer with a quote.

.................................................................................................................................................

.................................................................................................................................................

**Q3**  What does Margaret mean in each of the following quotes?

a)  **"Get you some of this distilled Carduus Benedictus, and lay it to your heart"**

Meaning: ........................................................................................................................................

.................................................................................................................................................

b)  **"methinks you look with your eyes as other women do"**

Meaning: ........................................................................................................................................

## Act 3, Scene 5 — Dogberry tries to tell Leonato about Don John's plot

**Q4**  Read lines 1-31.  Find a quote that shows Leonato is losing his patience with the Watch.

.................................................................................................................................................

**Q5**  What does Leonato ask Dogberry to do at the end of the scene?

.................................................................................................................................................

**Q6**  Why do you think Shakespeare ends Act 3 with this scene?  Explain your answer.

.................................................................................................................................................

.................................................................................................................................................

### *Beatrice and Benedick have a hate-love relationship...*

There's a lot going on in the plot in Act 3, and the mood varies from scene to scene.  Choose two times in Act 3 when the mood changes, then write a short explanation of how it changes each time.

# Act Four

## Act 4, Scene 1 — Claudio accuses Hero of being disloyal

**Q1** Put these events in order by numbering the boxes. The first one has been done for you.

Leonato asks the Friar to start the wedding ceremony quickly. `1`

Leonato is so ashamed that he asks "**Hath no man's dagger here a point for me?**"

Don Pedro explains that a man was seen at Hero's window the previous night.

Claudio interrupts the service to accuse Hero of being unfaithful.

Hero is confused by the accusation and questions Claudio.

**Q2** Why do you think Claudio goes along with the wedding ceremony at first before rejecting Hero? Explain your answer.

.........................................................................................................................................

.........................................................................................................................................

**Q3** Claudio exclaims "**Farewell, / Thou pure impiety and impious purity!**" after he rejects Hero. What is he suggesting about Hero?

© Donald Cooper/photostage

...........................................................................................

...........................................................................................

...........................................................................................

**Q4** Claudio leaves after Hero faints. Explain what impression this gives of Claudio.

.........................................................................................................................................

.........................................................................................................................................

**Q5** Find a quote that shows Beatrice doesn't believe the accusations against Hero. Explain what this suggests about Beatrice's attitude towards Hero.

Quote: ...........................................................................................................................

Explanation: ..................................................................................................................

.........................................................................................................................................

**Section One — Analysis of Acts**

## Act 4, Scene 1 continued — Benedick and Beatrice confess their love

**Q1** Why do you think Benedick stays after Don Pedro and Claudio leave? Explain your answer.

.........................................................................................................................................................

.........................................................................................................................................................

**Q2** Read lines 199-242. Why does Friar Francis want to pretend Hero is dead? Give two reasons.

1) ...................................................................................................................................................

.........................................................................................................................................................

2) ...................................................................................................................................................

.........................................................................................................................................................

**Q3** Benedick tells Beatrice he loves her after the wedding. Why do you think Shakespeare includes this moment at the end of this scene? Explain your answer.

.........................................................................................................................................................

.........................................................................................................................................................

.........................................................................................................................................................

## Act 4, Scene 2 — Dogberry questions Borachio and Conrade

**Q4** How does the Sexton manage to find out the truth about Don John's plot? Explain your answer.

.........................................................................................................................................................

.........................................................................................................................................................

**Q5** Find a quote that shows Don John flees after the wedding. Explain why he might have done this.

Quote: ...........................................................................................................................................

Explanation: ...................................................................................................................................

.........................................................................................................................................................

---

### *Not all Heros wear capes — some wear a wedding dress...*

Claudio accusing Hero brings the play to its dramatic climax. Choose three factors from earlier in the play that led up to this accusation, then write a few lines for each one explaining the effect it had.

# Act Five

## Act 5, Scene 1 — Leonato, Antonio and Benedick challenge Claudio

**Q1** Leonato tells Antonio **"let no comforter delight mine ear / But such a one whose wrongs do suit with mine"**. Summarise what this quote means, then explain why you think Leonato says this.

Meaning: ......................................................................................................................................................

..............................................................................................................................................................................

Explanation: ............................................................................................................................................

..............................................................................................................................................................................


**Q2** Find a quote to support the following statements.

**a)** Antonio thinks Leonato should seek revenge.

Quote: .........................................................................................................................................................

**b)** Leonato now believes Hero is innocent.

Quote: .........................................................................................................................................................

**c)** Claudio doesn't want to fight Leonato.

Quote: .........................................................................................................................................................


**Q3** Read lines 80-101. How does Antonio show that he is a loyal brother in this passage? Use a quote to support your answer.

..............................................................................................................................................................................

..............................................................................................................................................................................


**Q4** Claudio and Don Pedro make jokes and don't take Benedick seriously when he confronts them about Hero. Explain why their behaviour might seem inappropriate to the audience.

....................................................................................................

....................................................................................................

....................................................................................................

....................................................................................................

....................................................................................................

## Act 5, Scene 1 continued — Borachio reveals Don John's plot

**Q1** Read lines 178-199. In Act 2, Scene 3, Benedick says that men become foolish when they fall in love. How does the characters' behaviour in this passage suggest that idea is wrong? Explain your answer.

...........................................................................................................................................................

...........................................................................................................................................................

**Q2** Read lines 226-245. Why do you think Borachio confesses? Use a quote to support your answer.

...........................................................................................................................................................

...........................................................................................................................................................

...........................................................................................................................................................

**Q3** Explain what each of the quotes below suggests about Claudio at this point in the play.

| Quote | What it suggests about Claudio |
|---|---|
| a) "Sweet Hero! Now thy image doth appear / In the rare semblance that I loved it first." (lines 248-249) | |
| b) "Impose me to what penance your invention / Can lay upon my sin" (lines 270-271) | |
| c) "Yet sinned I not / But in mistaking." (lines 271-272) | |

**Q4** Why do you think Leonato is still angry with Claudio and Don Pedro after Borachio's confession?

...........................................................................................................................................................

...........................................................................................................................................................

**Q5** Read lines 276-289. Do you think Leonato's 'punishment' for Claudio is an appropriate response to Claudio's actions earlier in the play? Explain your answer.

...........................................................................................................................................................

...........................................................................................................................................................

**Section One — Analysis of Acts**

## Act 5, Scene 2 — Benedick tries to woo Beatrice

**Q1**    Read lines 1-23, then answer the following questions.

   **a)**  How does Benedick and Margaret's conversation create a light-hearted mood?

   ...............................................................................................................................................

   ...............................................................................................................................................

   **b)**  Margaret says Benedick's wit is "**as blunt as the fencer's foils, which hit, but hurt not**".
   In your own words, explain what she is suggesting about Benedick.

   ...............................................................................................................................................

**Q2**    Read lines 29-41.  What does Benedick's speech suggest about his feelings
for Beatrice at this point in the play?  Use a quote to support your answer.

   ...............................................................................................................................................

   ...............................................................................................................................................

   ...............................................................................................................................................

**Q3**    Which of the following statements best describe Benedick
and Beatrice's interaction in this scene?  Tick **two** boxes.

   Benedick and Beatrice no longer bicker now they have admitted their feelings.    ☐

   Benedick is confident when he speaks to Beatrice about his love for her.    ☐

   Beatrice makes it clear that she still thinks Benedick is flawed.    ☐

## Act 5, Scene 3 — Claudio mourns at Hero's tomb

**Q4**    Why do you think Shakespeare makes this scene so short?  Explain your answer.

   ...............................................................................................................................................

   ...............................................................................................................................................

**Q5**    How does the language in Balthasar's song help to create a sombre
mood in this scene?  Use a quote to support your answer.

   ...............................................................................................................................................

   ...............................................................................................................................................

   ...............................................................................................................................................

**Section One — Analysis of Acts**

## Act 5, Scene 4 — Hero is alive and Benedick proposes to Beatrice

**Q1** Put these events in order by numbering the boxes. The first one has been done for you.

Claudio and Don Pedro arrive and make fun of Benedick for being in love. ☐

Leonato instructs the women to wait in a "**chamber**" until he calls them. 1

Claudio promises to marry Hero's 'cousin' in front of Friar Francis. ☐

Benedick asks for Leonato's blessing to marry Beatrice. ☐

Hero takes off her mask and reveals she is alive. ☐

**Q2** Identify who said each of these phrases, then explain what each one means.

**a)** "**One Hero died defiled, but I do live**"  Said by: .............................................

Meaning: ....................................................................................................................

**b)** "**Here's our own hands against our hearts.**"  Said by: .............................................

Meaning: ....................................................................................................................

**Q3** Read lines 75-83. Benedick and Beatrice speak to each other in blank verse, which is associated with traditional courtly love. How does this suggest that their relationship has changed since Act 1? Explain your answer.

.................................................................................................................................

.................................................................................................................................

**Q4** Read lines 99-122. Why do you think Shakespeare makes Benedick seem so positive about the benefits of marriage in this passage? Explain your answer.

.................................................................................................................................

.................................................................................................................................

.................................................................................................................................

.................................................................................................................................

© Photo 12 / Alamy Stock Photo

**Q5** Why do you think Shakespeare only mentions Don John briefly at the end of the play?

.................................................................................................................................

### *Sounds more like Much Ado about Something to me...*

Now you've made it to the end of the play, write down the main events in *Much Ado About Nothing*. List your events in the order they happen in the play, and include at least three events from each act.

PRACTICE TASK

 ☐  ☐  ☐

**Section One — Analysis of Acts**

# Using Quotes

In the exam, you'll have to back up your points with quotes from the play. You won't have a copy of the text with you, so it's important to memorise some useful quotes. To really impress the examiner, you'll need to embed your quotes in your sentences so that they sound natural. This means picking out the parts of your quote that are the most relevant to your point and then including them in a sentence to back up that point. Have a go at these questions and you'll get the hang of it in no time.

**Q1** Read these statements about quotes.
Decide whether each one is **true** or **false**.

|  | True | False |
|---|---|---|
| All your quotes should be written exactly as they appear in the text. | ☐ | ☐ |
| An embedded quote is better than a quote added to the end of a sentence. | ☐ | ☐ |
| Quotes should simply repeat what you have written. | ☐ | ☐ |
| You should include lots of long quotes. | ☐ | ☐ |
| Your quotes don't necessarily need to back up your argument. | ☐ | ☐ |

**Q2** Rewrite the following sentences so that a short part of the quote is embedded in each one.
The first one has been done for you.

| Sentence | Quote | New sentence |
|---|---|---|
| **a)** Don John is a dishonourable character who aims to cause trouble for everyone else. | "it must not be denied but I am a plain-dealing villain" | Don John is a "plain-dealing villain" who aims to cause trouble for everyone else. |
| **b)** Don Pedro believes that being high-born makes Benedick a suitable husband for Beatrice. | "Thus far I can praise him — he is of a noble strain" | |
| **c)** Hero says it will be easy to damage Beatrice's reputation by gossiping about her. | "I'll devise some honest slanders / To stain my cousin with" | |
| **d)** Leonato believes Hero's unfaithfulness is undeniable once Beatrice admits that she didn't sleep in Hero's bed. | "O, that is stronger made / Which was before barred up with ribs of iron!" | |
| **e)** Benedick writes poetry, which suggests that he wants to woo Beatrice. | "A halting sonnet of his own pure brain, / Fashioned to Beatrice" | |

# P.E.E.D.

P.E.E.D. is a great way for you to structure your answers — it makes your paragraphs more concise and analytical.  In each of your paragraphs, you need to make a **point**, give a supporting **example**, then **explain** how this example backs up your argument.  Finally, to really impress the examiner, you need to **develop** your point by explaining its effect on the audience, or its links to themes, context or other events in the play.  Here are a couple of exercises to help you get to grips with P.E.E.D.

**Q1**  Neither of the sample answers below have used P.E.E.D. correctly.
For each, say which stage of P.E.E.D. is missing.

**a)**

> Shakespeare uses Dogberry's language to present him as incompetent.
> In Act 5, Scene 1, Dogberry says the same thing in six ways when reporting
> Borachio and Conrade's crimes.  His incompetence is reinforced by his
> misuse of words, such as when he says "secondarily" instead of 'secondly'.

Missing stage: .................................................

**b)**

> Shakespeare uses staging to present Hero as submissive.  Hero is on stage during the first
> half of the opening scene, when Beatrice and several male characters are discussing the
> war and marriage, but she only has one line of dialogue.  The fact that Hero is visible to the
> audience but stays silent suggests that she is willing to go along with the others' opinions.

Missing stage: ..............................................

**Q2**  Fill in the missing steps in the P.E.E.D. structures below.

**a)** Point:  Claudio's funeral poem in Act 5, Scene 3 shows how harmful false rumours can be.

Example:  In his poem, Claudio claims that "slanderous tongues" have caused Hero's death.

Explain: ..................................................................................................

Develop:  In Act 4, Scene 1, Shakespeare suggests that the harmful effects of false rumours
can be long-lasting by comparing them to "ink" which permanently stains Hero's character.

**b)** Point:  Shakespeare emphasises Beatrice's wit in Act 2, Scene 1.

Example: ..................................................................................................

Explain:  Here, Beatrice's dialogue includes a clever pun, which shows she is quick-witted.

Develop:  Beatrice's witty remarks and playful use of language highlight her lively
and spirited nature, which might make her seem more likeable to the audience.

# Section Two — Characters

## Hero

**Q1** Fill in the gaps in the table below. The first one has been done for you.

| Event in the play | What it suggests about Hero |
|---|---|
| **a)** Hero offers to do "**any modest office**" to help Beatrice marry a good husband. | She is kind and cares about her cousin. |
| **b)** Hero insists on wearing the wedding dress of her choice when Margaret tries to talk her out of it. | |
| **c)** Hero faints when Claudio publicly shames her. | |

**Q2** Read Hero's aside in Act 3, Scene 1, lines 105-106.
What does it suggest about Hero's attitude to love?

.......................................................................................................................................................

.......................................................................................................................................................

**Q3** Read Act 4, Scene 1, lines 76-85. How does Hero's language in this passage show how shocked she is by Claudio's accusations? Use a quote to support your answer.

.......................................................................................................................................................

.......................................................................................................................................................

.......................................................................................................................................................

**Q4** Hero marries Claudio at the end of the play, even though he has harmed her. Why might she have done this? Explain your answer.

.................................................................................................

.................................................................................................

.................................................................................................

.................................................................................................

---

> **PRACTICE TASK**
>
> ### *Alright, you can stop holding out now — she's here...*
>
> Read Act 2, Scene 1, lines 82-96. Write an essay plan for this question: **Starting with this extract, explain how Shakespeare presents Hero in *Much Ado About Nothing*.** You should write about:
> * how Hero is presented in the extract
> * how Hero is presented in the rest of the play.

# Claudio

**Q1** Look at these statements about Claudio.
Decide which are **true** and which are **false**.

| | True | False |
|---|---|---|
| Claudio is presented as a brave soldier. | ☐ | ☐ |
| He questions everything that he hears. | ☐ | ☐ |
| He makes decisions impulsively. | ☐ | ☐ |
| Social status is less important to him than love. | ☐ | ☐ |
| Claudio quickly sees the error of his ways. | ☐ | ☐ |

© Nigel Norrington / ArenaPAL

**Q2** For each character below, explain how they feel about Claudio in the scene that is given in brackets. Find a quote from the relevant scene to support each answer.

**a)** Don John (Act 1, Scene 3): ...................................................................................................

...............................................................................................................................................

Quote: ..................................................................................................................................

**b)** Hero (Act 3, Scene 1): ..................................................................................................

...............................................................................................................................................

Quote: ..................................................................................................................................

**Q3** Explain how Shakespeare makes Claudio seem overly suspicious in Act 2, Scene 1. Use an example to support your answer.

...............................................................................................................................................

...............................................................................................................................................

...............................................................................................................................................

**Q4** Read Act 4, Scene 1, lines 28-60. Why is Claudio so angry when he thinks Hero has been disloyal? Explain your answer.

...............................................................................................................................................

...............................................................................................................................................

...............................................................................................................................................

---

PRACTICE TASK

### *"Claudio, Claudio, wherefor—" Oops, sorry, wrong play...*

Shakespeare presents Claudio as a romantic hero, but he still has flaws. Write a paragraph giving two examples of times in the play when the audience might respond negatively to Claudio's actions.

 ☐   ☐   ☐

# Beatrice

**Q1** Read the paragraph below and fill in the gaps using words from the box.

In the play, Shakespeare presents Beatrice as outspoken, ............................ and clever.

She ............................ against 16th-century stereotypes about women by declaring that

she "**could not endure**" a husband and using her ............................ to criticise male

characters. This shows the audience that Beatrice is a strong character, as she is not

............................ of ............................ society's expectations.

| defying | wit | worrying | assertive | charm | timid | rebels | ignores | afraid | malicious |

**Q2** Briefly explain how and why Beatrice's attitude to marriage has changed by the end of the play.

..................................................................................................................................

..................................................................................................................................

**Q3** Read Act 3, Scene 1, lines 107-116. How might this passage affect the audience's view of Beatrice? Explain your answer.

..........................................................................

..........................................................................

..........................................................................

..........................................................................

© Donald Cooper/photostage

**Q4** Identify who said each of these phrases, then explain what they reveal about Beatrice.

**a)** "**Disdain and scorn ride sparkling in her eyes**"    Said by: ............................

Explanation: ..................................................................................................

**b)** "**Lady Beatrice, have you wept all this while?**"    Said by: ............................

Explanation: ..................................................................................................

---

**MAKING LINKS**

### *I like to imagine Beatrice's surname is "-ratops"\*...*

Beatrice's behaviour often contrasts with that of Hero, who tries to behave in a socially acceptable way. This contrast reinforces the idea that Beatrice is an unconventional 16th-century woman.

*Roar.

# Benedick

**Q1** Find a quote that supports each of the following statements.

**a)** Benedick admires Beatrice's wit.

Quote: ...................................................................................................................................................

**b)** Benedick speaks unfavourably about women.

Quote: ...................................................................................................................................................

**c)** Benedick has a high opinion of himself.

Quote: ...................................................................................................................................................

**Q2** Do you think Benedick is a proud man? Give a reason for your answer.

.....................................................................................................................................................................

.....................................................................................................................................................................

**Q3** Read Act 5, Scene 1, lines 144-190. What does this passage tell
the audience about Benedick's character? Explain your answer.

.....................................................................................................................................................................

.....................................................................................................................................................................

**Q4** Read Act 2, Scene 3. Explain how Benedick's attitude
to love changes from the start to the end of this scene.
Use a quote to support your answer.

..........................................................................................................

..........................................................................................................

..........................................................................................................

..........................................................................................................

© Nigel Norrington / ArenaPAL

---

EXAM PRACTICE

## "I am well" — Benedick loves imitating water features...

Read Act 2, Scene 1, lines 229-255. **How is Benedick presented as sensitive by Shakespeare in**
*Much Ado About Nothing*? You should write about:

- how Shakespeare presents Benedick as sensitive in this extract
- how Benedick is presented as sensitive in the play as a whole.

## Don Pedro

**Q1** Briefly describe an event in the play where Don Pedro is:

**a)** authoritative

.................................................................................................

.................................................................................................

**b)** kind

.................................................................................................

.................................................................................................

© BBC / AF archive / Alamy Stock Photo

**Q2** Read Act 2, Scene 1, lines 331-375. How does Shakespeare give the impression that Don Pedro is a playful character in this passage? Support your answer with a quote.

.............................................................................................................................

.............................................................................................................................

.............................................................................................................................

.............................................................................................................................

**Q3** How does Shakespeare show that Don Pedro is honourable?
Use a quote to support your answer.

.............................................................................................................................

.............................................................................................................................

.............................................................................................................................

**Q4** Don Pedro doesn't apologise to Leonato until he sees proof that he was mistaken about Hero. What does this tell the audience about his character?

.............................................................................................................................

.............................................................................................................................

### *Before there were dating apps, there was Don Pedro...*

If you're writing about Don Pedro, think about the different sides to his character. He's a loyal friend and a powerful prince, but he also looks foolish when he falls for Don John's trick and shames Hero.

# Don John

**Q1** Read the following statements about Don John,
then decide which are **true** and which are **false**.

|  | True | False |
|---|---|---|
| Don John is a cheerful character. | ☐ | ☐ |
| He is bitter about losing the war to Don Pedro, Claudio and Benedick. | ☐ | ☐ |
| Don John considers himself to be a good person. | ☐ | ☐ |
| Don John enjoys disrupting other characters' lives. | ☐ | ☐ |
| Lying to people is difficult for Don John. | ☐ | ☐ |

**Q2** Find a quote that supports each of the following statements.

**a)** Don John's relationship with his brother is poor.

Quote: ................................................................................................................

**b)** Don John has a negative opinion of marriage.

Quote: ................................................................................................................

**Q3** Read Act 1, Scene 3, lines 61-65. What impression might the audience get
of Don John's character in this passage? Use a quote to support your answer.

................................................................................................................

................................................................................................................

................................................................................................................

................................................................................................................

**Q4** In the 16th century, illegitimate children like Don John had
little power in their family or in society. How might this help to
explain Don John's behaviour in the play? Explain your answer.

................................................................................................................

................................................................................................................

................................................................................................................

© Donald Cooper/photostage

---

### *Brussels sprouts are food to my displeasure...*

At the end of the play, the audience is told that Don John has been captured. This is linked to the
play's form as a comedy — as part of the happy ending, the villain doesn't get away with his crimes.

 ☐   ☐   ☐

**Section Two — Characters**

# Leonato

**Q1** Fill in the gaps in the table below. The first one has been done for you.

| Event in the play | What it suggests about Leonato |
|---|---|
| **a)** Leonato warmly welcomes all of his visitors, including Don John. (Act 1, Scene 1) | Leonato is friendly, kind and respectful. |
| **b)** Leonato enthusiastically takes part in tricking Benedick. (Act 2, Scene 3) | |
| **c)** Leonato is willing to fight Claudio to defend Hero's honour. (Act 5, Scene 1) | |

**Q2** Find a quote from the play to back up each of these statements.

**a)** Leonato is happy for Hero to marry Claudio.

Quote: ................................................................................................................................

**b)** Leonato thinks it's important for Beatrice to find a husband.

Quote: ................................................................................................................................

**Q3** How does Shakespeare present Leonato as caring?
Use an example to support your answer.

.............................................................................................

.............................................................................................

.............................................................................................

.............................................................................................

© Donald Cooper/photostage

**Q4** Read Act 4, Scene 1, lines 119-142. Why do you think Leonato is so
quick to believe the accusations against Hero? Explain your answer.

.............................................................................................................................

.............................................................................................................................

.............................................................................................................................

### "FIGHT ME, CLAUDIO" — Leonato (probably)...

Writing about Leonato gives you lots of chances to mention context. Throughout the play, Leonato
demonstrates 16th-century society's different expectations of a host, a father, a governor and a man.

# Dogberry

**Q1** Find a quote from Act 4, Scene 2 that shows Dogberry is:

**a)** easily offended

Quote: ........................................................................................

**b)** a leader

Quote: ........................................................................................

**c)** a comic character

Quote: ........................................................................................

© Donald Cooper/photostage

**Q2** How does Shakespeare show that Dogberry is proud of his status as a constable? Use a quote to support your answer.

........................................................................................

........................................................................................

**Q3** 'Shakespeare uses Dogberry to criticise people who have a low social status.' Do you agree with this statement? Give a reason for your answer.

........................................................................................

........................................................................................

........................................................................................

........................................................................................

**Q4** Why do you think Shakespeare has such an incompetent character uncover the truth about Don John's plot? Give a reason for your answer.

........................................................................................

........................................................................................

........................................................................................

**PRACTICE TASK**

## You can't teach a Dogberry ~~new tricks~~ correct English...

Dogberry makes lots of mistakes with language in the play, but they're not just there to create humour. Identify a time when his language mistakes affect the plot of the play, then explain how they do this.

# Other Characters

**Q1** Read Act 3, Scene 4, lines 17-36.  What impression
does the audience get of Margaret in this passage?

.......................................................................................................................................................

.......................................................................................................................................................

**Q2** Read the paragraph below and fill in the gaps using the words in the box.

Shakespeare often uses minor characters in *Much Ado About Nothing* to help ...........................

the plot.  For example, in Act 3, Scene 1, the presence of ........................... allows Hero to be

........................... of Beatrice, which is a key part of the plan to trick Beatrice into loving

Benedick.  Similarly, Borachio's boasting to Conrade allows the Watch to discover Don John's

..........................., which results in Don John being brought to ........................... in Act 5.

| | | | | | | | | | |
|---|---|---|---|---|---|---|---|---|---|
| Margaret | limit | admiring | deception | provide | justice | develop | critical | Ursula | court |

**Q3** Do you think Borachio is more to blame for the plot to shame
Hero than Don John?  Give a reason for your answer.

.......................................................................................................................................................

.......................................................................................................................................................

.......................................................................................................................................................

**Q4** Read Act 4, Scene 1, lines 154-169.  How does Shakespeare
emphasise Friar Francis's belief in Hero's innocence?
Use an example from the text to support your answer.

.............................................................................................

.............................................................................................

.............................................................................................

.............................................................................................

.............................................................................................

*Francis does a cracking breakfast — he's a great Fryer...*

It might not seem important to talk about minor characters, but it shows the examiner you have an
in-depth knowledge of the play.  Consider how these minor characters are used to develop the plot.

**Section Two — Characters**

# Making Links

A really good way to improve your answers is to make links between your point and different parts of the play. You can do this in lots of different ways, including making links between characters, events or themes. This page will get you thinking about how some of the main characters behave in different parts of the play. Try to only use specific examples — it'll make your points much more convincing.

**Q1** Think about how Beatrice and Benedick change over the course of the play. Give an example from Act 1 which shows what each character is like, then give an example from Act 5 which shows how they have changed.

| Character | Act 1 | Act 5 |
|---|---|---|
| Beatrice | | |
| Benedick | | |

**Q2** Some characters don't change much. For each character below, give a word to describe their personality. Then find two examples from different parts of the play that support each of your descriptions. These could be quotes or examples of things that happen.

| Character | Personality | Example One | Example Two |
|---|---|---|---|
| Hero | | | |
| Claudio | | | |
| Don Pedro | | | |
| Don John | | | |

# Practice Questions

*Here are some exciting exam-style questions to sink your teeth into — lucky you. There's quite a lot to be getting on with, so make a plan of all of the points that you're going to write about in each question before you start writing your answer. You don't need to do them all in one go, though. What a relief that is, eh?*

**Q1** Read the extract below from Act 2, Scene 1. How is Beatrice presented as passionate in *Much Ado About Nothing*? You should refer to this extract and to the rest of the play.

| | |
|---|---|
| **Beatrice:** | Just, if he send me no husband, for the which blessing I am at him upon my knees every morning and evening. Lord, I could not endure a husband with a beard on his face — I had rather lie in the woollen. |
| **Leonato:** | You may light on a husband that hath no beard. |
| **Beatrice:** | What should I do with him? Dress him in my apparel and make him my waiting-gentlewoman? He that hath a beard is more than a youth, and he that hath no beard is less than a man; and he that is more than a youth is not for me, and he that is less than a man, I am not for him. Therefore, I will even take sixpence in earnest of the bearward, and lead his apes into hell. |
| **Leonato:** | Well, then, go you into hell? |
| **Beatrice:** | No, but to the gate — and there will the devil meet me, like an old cuckold, with horns on his head, and say 'Get you to heaven, Beatrice, get you to heaven. Here's no place for you maids.' |

(Act 2, Scene 1, lines 26-44)

**Q2** Read Act 1, Scene 1, lines 151-176. To what extent are Benedick and Claudio presented as opposites in *Much Ado About Nothing*? Refer to the extract and to the play as a whole.

**Q3** Read Act 2, Scene 1, lines 256-294, then answer the questions below.

**a)** Explain how Don Pedro's relationship with his followers is presented in this extract.

**b)** In this extract, Don Pedro observes that Benedick and Claudio are upset. What is the significance of making observations in the rest of the play? You should consider:
- times when characters are observant or unobservant
- how this influences the characters' actions.

**Q4** Read Act 5, Scene 1, lines 1-32. How is Leonato presented as mature in the play? Refer to the extract and to the play as a whole.

**Section Two — Characters**

## Honour and Reputation

**Q1** Fill in the gaps in the paragraph below using the words in the box.

A good reputation is important to most of the .......................... characters.

Shakespeare suggests that the desire to gain honour can be ..........................,

as it inspires Claudio to fight bravely in ........................... However, Claudio's

desperation to protect his reputation makes him act ..........................,

such as when he easily believes Don John's lies about ...........................

> minor
> humorous
> battle
> foolishly
> admirable
> Hero
> male
> Leonato

**Q2** Why does Leonato challenge Claudio to a duel in Act 5, Scene 1? Refer to honour in your answer.

..........................................................................................................................

..........................................................................................................................

**Q3** Honour and reputation play a part in Hero's treatment when Claudio rejects her at the wedding. Read from the start of Act 4, Scene 1 to line 153, then answer the following questions.

**a)** Explain how honour and reputation influence Don Pedro's behaviour in this passage.

..........................................................................................

..........................................................................................

..........................................................................................

..........................................................................................

**b)** Most of the characters don't believe that Hero is innocent. Why do you think they believe Don Pedro and Claudio over her? Use an example from the text to support your answer.

..........................................................................................................................

..........................................................................................................................

..........................................................................................................................

..........................................................................................................................

---

### *Poor Hero — everyone's honour case...*

The theme of honour affects lots of different characters throughout the play. Don John's lies about Hero don't just damage her reputation — they threaten Claudio's, Don Pedro's and Leonato's as well.

# Love and Marriage

**Q1** Read the following statements about love and marriage in
the play. Decide whether each statement is **true** or **false**.

|  | True | False |
|---|---|---|
| Characters worry about their unmarried friends and relatives. | ☐ | ☐ |
| Hero and Beatrice must behave in a certain way to be seen as suitable wives. | ☐ | ☐ |
| In the play, social status is seen as irrelevant to finding a partner. | ☐ | ☐ |
| The characters are happy to have long engagements and wait to get married. | ☐ | ☐ |

**Q2** In the 16th century, women often had no choice about who they married. Explain how this is
reflected in the play through Hero and Claudio's relationship. Support your answer with a quote.

© Donald Cooper/photostage

.................................................................................................

.................................................................................................

.................................................................................................

.................................................................................................

.................................................................................................

**Q3** Read the examples from the play below. What does each example
suggest about Claudio's attitude to getting married? Explain your answer.

**a)** Claudio asks whether Leonato has a son, and is told that Hero is his **"only heir"**.

.................................................................................................

.................................................................................................

**b)** Claudio agrees to marry Hero's 'cousin' even though he has never met her.

.................................................................................................

.................................................................................................

**Q4** How does Shakespeare suggest that Benedick and Beatrice have a more
meaningful relationship than Claudio and Hero? Explain your answer.

.................................................................................................

.................................................................................................

.................................................................................................

**Q5**   Fill in the gaps in the paragraph below by using the words in the box.

Courtly love was a traditional way for a man to ........................... a woman

he hoped to marry.  Claudio ........................... courtly love traditions, while

Benedick initially ........................... them.  Shakespeare suggests that courtly

love leads to relationships that are ..........................., as the man would

praise and flatter the woman but often didn't ........................... her very well.

| |
|---|
| annoy |
| superficial |
| woo |
| ignores |
| follows |
| marriage |
| forgets |
| know |

**Q6**   Read Act 1, Scene 1, lines 278-293.  What impression does Shakespeare give
of love in this passage?  Use an example from the text to support your answer.

........................................................................................................................

........................................................................................................................

........................................................................................................................

........................................................................................................................

**Q7**   Read Act 5, Scene 2, lines 44-69.  What does Benedick and Beatrice's bickering
in this passage suggest about love?  Support your answer with a quote.

........................................................................................................................

........................................................................................................................

........................................................................................................................

**Q8**   After the tricks to make Benedick and Beatrice fall in love with each other, Benedick says
he has "**toothache**" and Beatrice says she is "**sick**".  What do these references to physical
illness suggest about how Benedick and Beatrice feel about love?  Explain your answer.

........................................................................................................................

........................................................................................................................

........................................................................................................................

### It's courtly love for Claudio — he's rubbish at tennis...

Imagine you're Claudio and you're madly in love with Hero.  Write a letter to Leonato asking for his
permission to marry her.  Try to use arguments a 16th-century father would have found convincing.

**Section Three — Context and Themes**

# Deception and Misunderstanding

**Q1** For each character, describe a time in the play when they deceive another character, then explain what this suggests about their attitude to deception. The first one has been done for you.

| Character | Example of deception | Attitude to deception |
|---|---|---|
| **a)** Leonato | He tells Claudio to mourn at Hero's tomb even though she isn't really dead. | He views deception as a tool to restore Hero's honour and her marriage to Claudio. |
| **b)** Borachio | | |
| **c)** Hero | | |

**Q2** Read Act 4, Scene 2, lines 42-49, then answer the following questions.

**a)** Explain the misunderstanding that takes place in this passage.

........................................................................................................................................

........................................................................................................................................

**b)** How does this misunderstanding create humour for the audience?

........................................................................................................................................

........................................................................................................................................

**Q3** When Benedick is tricked in Act 2, Scene 3, Claudio says to "**Bait the hook well — this fish will bite.**" What does this suggest about the deception in this scene?

........................................................................................................................................

........................................................................................................................................

**Q4** Benedick and Beatrice are both deceived by their friends in the play. Why might the audience respond positively to these deceptions? Explain your answer.

........................................................................................................

........................................................................................................

........................................................................................................

........................................................................................................

© Donald Cooper/photostage

**Section Three — Context and Themes**

**Q5** Find a quote to back up each of these statements about the masked ball in Act 2, Scene 1.

 **a)** The masked ball gives characters the chance to speak openly.

 Quote: ................................................................................................................................

 **b)** Not all of the characters are skilled at deception.

 Quote: ................................................................................................................................

**Q6** Which of the following statements best describe how
Shakespeare presents deception in the play? Tick **two** boxes.

 Deception and trickery are shown to always cause harm to other people. ☐

 Even honourable characters can become involved in deception. ☐

 Characters who deceive others are all shown to be punished at the end of the play. ☐

 Most characters fail to recognise when they are being deceived. ☐

**Q7** In Act 4, Scene 1, Friar Francis realises Hero is innocent by "**noting**" (observing) her.
Characters often 'note' things and misunderstand them. Why do you think that
Shakespeare makes a reference to 'noting' at this point in the play?

 ................................................................................................................................

 ................................................................................................................................

**Q8** In Act 4, Scene 1, Claudio says that Hero is "**most foul, most fair**".
Explain what this suggests about appearances and reality.

 ................................................................................................................................

 ................................................................................................................................

**Q9** In Act 5, Scene 4, Claudio believes he is marrying Hero's 'cousin'. Why do you think
Shakespeare has deception bring about the play's ending? Explain your answer.

 ................................................................................................................................

 ................................................................................................................................

 ................................................................................................................................

## *Dogberry's still waiting to meet Misterunderstanding...*

Read Act 1, Scene 2, lines 1-25. **Explore how misunderstandings are presented in the play.**
You should consider:
- how misunderstandings are presented in this extract
- how misunderstandings are presented in the play as a whole.

 ☐  ☐  ☐

# Gender

**Q1** In the 16th century, women were expected to obey their fathers. Give three examples of times when Leonato makes a decision about Hero's life without consulting her.

1)...................................................................................................................................................

2)...................................................................................................................................................

3)...................................................................................................................................................

**Q2** In Shakespeare's time, women were expected to get married. For each of the statements below, describe how an Elizabethan audience might have reacted to the event and explain your answer.

**a)** In Act 2, Scene 1, Beatrice rejects Don Pedro's offer of marriage.

............................................................................................................................................................

............................................................................................................................................................

**b)** Beatrice makes it clear that she doesn't want a husband, but the other characters ignore her wishes and make a plan to help her get married.

............................................................................................................................................................

............................................................................................................................................................

**Q3** Read the statements below about how women were expected to behave in the 16th century. For each, describe one event from the play that shows a character conforming to this expectation and one event that shows a character defying this expectation.

| Gender expectation | Example of conforming | Example of defying |
|---|---|---|
| **a)** Women were expected to be 'pure'. | | |
| **b)** Women were expected to be quiet and gentle. | | |

**Q4** The men in the play are influenced by society's expectations. Give an example from the play that suggests there is an expectation that men should want to get married.

............................................................................................................................................................

............................................................................................................................................................

**Q5** The male characters in the play often make jokes about cuckolds. Explain how this shows their negative attitude towards women.

> In Shakespeare's time, a man with an unfaithful wife was called a cuckold.

..............................................................................................................................................

..............................................................................................................................................

..............................................................................................................................................

**Q6** Answer the following questions about Hero's behaviour in the play.

   **a)** How does Hero behave in the following scenes?

Act 1, Scene 1: ....................................................................................................................

Act 3, Scene 1: ....................................................................................................................

   **b)** Why do you think Hero's behaviour is different in Act 3, Scene 1? Refer to gender in your answer.

..............................................................................................................................................

..............................................................................................................................................

**Q7** In Act 4, Scene 1, Beatrice says **"O God, that I were a man!"** Why do you think she says this? Explain your answer.

..............................................................................................................................................

..............................................................................................................................................

**Q8** 'Beatrice marrying Benedick is a happy ending for her character.' Do you agree with this statement? Explain your answer.

...............................................................................................

...............................................................................................

...............................................................................................

...............................................................................................

...............................................................................................

---

### *Who run the Shakespearean world? Not girls...*

If you're writing about gender, think about the expectations that an Elizabethan audience would have had about men and women, and how the characters in the play conform to or defy these stereotypes.

# Loyalty

**Q1** For each of the following characters, explain how the quote makes them seem loyal.

| Character | Quote | How this makes them seem loyal |
|---|---|---|
| **a)** Beatrice | **"Kill Claudio."** (Act 4, Scene 1, line 287) | |
| **b)** Don Pedro | **"I will join with thee to disgrace her"** (Act 3, Scene 2, lines 116-117) | |

**Q2** Don Pedro forgives Don John after the war. Why do you think he gives him a second chance? Explain your answer.

© Nigel Norrington / ArenaPAL

.............................................................................

.............................................................................

.............................................................................

**Q3** In Act 1, Scene 1, Beatrice mocks Benedick by saying **"He hath every month a new sworn brother."** What does this suggest about Beatrice's attitude to loyalty? Explain your answer.

.............................................................................................................

.............................................................................................................

.............................................................................................................

**Q4** Read Act 2, Scene 1, lines 282-294, then answer the following questions.

**a)** How does Shakespeare highlight Don Pedro's loyalty to Claudio in this passage?

.............................................................................................................

.............................................................................................................

**b)** How might the audience react to Claudio's disloyalty and mistrust in this passage?

.............................................................................................................

.............................................................................................................

### *If you ever lose your back, Beatrice has probably got it...*

MAKING LINKS

The men in the play believe in following a code of honour, and loyalty to one another is a key part of this code. This leads to an inner conflict for Benedick when Beatrice asks him to fight Claudio for her.

# Writing about Context

To get a high mark in the exam, you'll need to discuss the context of *Much Ado About Nothing*. The play was written at the end of the 16th century, when expectations for men and women were more restrictive than they are today. You need to show the examiner that you understand how context might have influenced Shakespeare when he was writing and how it might affect different audiences.

**Q1** Read the sample answer extracts below and underline the contextual information.

> **a)** Shakespeare uses the Watch to create humour. In Act 3, Scene 5, Dogberry tells Leonato that one man must "ride behind" whenever "two men ride of a horse". Dogberry uses this metaphor to suggest that Verges is less intelligent than him, but the audience has already seen that both men are inept. This creates dramatic irony that is amusing for the audience. Shakespeare uses his presentation of the Watch in the play to mock the real Elizabethan Watch, who were generally considered to be useless.

> **b)** Don John is presented as manipulative. In Act 3, Scene 2, Don John encourages Claudio to doubt Hero's loyalty by telling him that Hero is "Leonato's Hero, your Hero, every man's Hero". Don John's list emphasises the idea that Hero 'belongs' to many different men and is not fully committed to Claudio. This plays on Claudio's fear of being cuckolded, which was a serious concern for men in Shakespeare's time. The fact that Claudio is so easily manipulated highlights his lack of confidence in Hero, which reflects the belief held by many men in the 16th century that women were untrustworthy.

**Q2** The answer extract below forms the first three parts of a P.E.E.D. paragraph (see p.17). Read through it and choose the most appropriate piece of context from the numbered list to develop the paragraph. Then write a short explanation of how your chosen piece of context relates to the rest of the paragraph.

> Shakespeare presents Beatrice as outspoken. In Act 2, Scene 3, Beatrice tells Benedick that she takes as much "pleasure" in asking him to come to dinner as could be placed on a "knife's point". This scathing comment highlights that Beatrice is not afraid to insult and challenge men, which sets her apart from the other female characters in the play.

1) Elizabeth I had ruled England for decades when *Much Ado About Nothing* was written.

2) England was under the leadership of a powerful female monarch when Shakespeare wrote *Much Ado About Nothing*, which might have influenced his presentation of women.

3) In the 16th century, women were expected to remain virgins until they were married.

Piece of context: .....................

Explanation of choice: ..........................................................................................................

..........................................................................................................................................

..........................................................................................................................................

..........................................................................................................................................

# Practice Questions

*You've made it to the end of another section — phew! Time to reward yourself with a few exam-style questions. You don't have to do them in order, so pick the one you'd like to tackle first, and away you go.*

**Q1** Read the extract below from Act 3, Scene 2. How does Shakespeare use the character of Claudio to explore ideas about loyalty? Refer to the extract and to the play as a whole.

| | |
|---|---|
| **Don John:** | I came hither to tell you, and, circumstances shortened, for she has been too long a talking of, the lady is disloyal. |
| **Claudio:** | Who, Hero? |
| **Don John:** | Even she — Leonato's Hero, your Hero, every man's Hero. |
| **Claudio:** | Disloyal? |
| **Don John:** | The word is too good to paint out her wickedness. I could say she were worse; think you of a worse title, and I will fit her to it. Wonder not till further warrant. Go but with me tonight, you shall see her chamber window entered, even the night before her wedding day. If you love her then, tomorrow wed her; but it would better fit your honour to change your mind. |
| **Claudio:** | May this be so? |
| **Don Pedro:** | I will not think it. |
| **Don John:** | If you dare not trust that you see, confess not that you know. If you will follow me, I will show you enough, and when you have seen more and heard more, proceed accordingly. |
| **Claudio:** | If I see any thing tonight why I should not marry her, tomorrow in the congregation, where I should wed, there will I shame her. |

(Act 3, Scene 2, lines 92-115)

**Q2** Read Act 4, Scene 1, lines 145-183, then answer the questions below.

**a)** Explain how ideas about innocence are presented in this extract.

**b)** In this extract, Leonato believes the accusations against Hero because they come from two princes and a count. Write about the importance of social status in the rest of the play. You should consider:
- times when a character's social status is presented
- how social status influences events in the play.

**Q3** Read Act 3, Scene 1, lines 26-56. 'The play's female characters behave as an Elizabethan audience would have expected them to.' How far do you agree with this statement? You should refer to the extract and to the rest of the play in your answer.

**Q4** Read Act 2, Scene 2, lines 21-49. How does Shakespeare explore ideas about honour in this extract and in the play as a whole?

## Form and Structure

**Q1** *Much Ado About Nothing* contains lots of features that are often found in Shakespeare's comedies. Give an example from the play for each of the features listed below.

Disguises: ..............................................................................................................................................

Music: ....................................................................................................................................................

Puns and wordplay: ..............................................................................................................................

..............................................................................................................................................................

**Q2** Decide if the following statements are **true** or **false**.

| | True | False |
|---|---|---|
| *Much Ado About Nothing* follows one main plot and has no subplots. | ☐ | ☐ |
| Shakespeare introduces obstacles for the couples to overcome during the play. | ☐ | ☐ |
| The play's form means that the audience anticipate a tragic ending. | ☐ | ☐ |

**Q3** Read Act 4, Scene 2, then answer the questions below about Shakespeare's use of comedy in *Much Ado About Nothing*.

**a)** Shakespeare's comedies often include comic characters whose main purpose is to make the audience laugh. Explain how Shakespeare uses Dogberry to create comedy in this scene.

..............................................................................................

..............................................................................................

..............................................................................................

**b)** Why do you think Shakespeare places a comic scene at this particular moment in the play? Explain your answer.

..............................................................................................................................................................

..............................................................................................................................................................

**Q4** Why do you think Shakespeare includes elements of tragedy in the play? Use an example from the text to support your answer.

..............................................................................................................................................................

..............................................................................................................................................................

..............................................................................................................................................................

**Q5** Read the paragraph below and fill in the gaps using words from the box.

In the first two acts of *Much Ado About Nothing*, Shakespeare develops the

............................... between the play's two main couples, Claudio and Hero

and Benedick and Beatrice. In Act 3, Don John's plot threatens to discredit

..............................., which builds ............................... This sets up the play's

dramatic ..............................., in which Claudio ............................... Hero.

> tension
> Beatrice
> tragedy
> rejects
> Hero
> climax
> forgives
> relationships
> ending

**Q6** Act 2, Scene 1 begins with the characters discussing how "**melancholy**" Don John is. Why do you think Shakespeare starts Act 2 in this way? Explain your answer.

............................................................................................................................

............................................................................................................................

............................................................................................................................

**Q7** Read Act 1, Scene 1, lines 298-310 and Act 2, Scene 1, lines 364-375. How do these passages encourage the audience to compare Claudio and Hero's relationship with Benedick and Beatrice's? Refer to the structure of the play in your answer.

............................................................................................................................

............................................................................................................................

............................................................................................................................

**Q8** The pace of the action increases towards the end of the play. Explain what effect this has on the audience.

............................................................................................................................

............................................................................................................................

**Q9** The play ends with "**pipers**" and a "***Dance***". Explain why you think Shakespeare does this.

............................................................................................................................

............................................................................................................................

### The real tragedy is that Hero ends up with Claudio...

When you're writing about structure, don't just describe what happens at different points in the play — think about why the scenes are ordered in the way they are and the effects that this order creates.

# Dramatic Irony

**Q1** Complete the table below by explaining how each of the examples creates dramatic irony and describing the effect that each one has on the audience.

> Dramatic irony is when the audience knows something that a character doesn't.

| Example from the play | How dramatic irony is created | Effect on the audience |
|---|---|---|
| **a)** Claudio says "'**Tis certain so, the prince woos for himself.**" (Act 2, Scene 1) | | |
| **b)** Dogberry tells Conrade "**I am a wise fellow**" (Act 4, Scene 2) | | |

**Q2** Shakespeare uses soliloquies to create dramatic irony in the play. Read Act 2, Scene 3, lines 219-246, then answer the questions below.

> A soliloquy is when a character speaks alone on stage.

a) Explain how the first line of Benedick's soliloquy creates dramatic irony.

.......................................................................................................................................................

.......................................................................................................................................................

b) Benedick says that he can "**spy some marks of love**" in Beatrice. Why might the audience find this funny?

.......................................................................................................

.......................................................................................................

.......................................................................................................

.......................................................................................................

**Q3** In *Much Ado About Nothing*, the audience always knows that Hero is innocent. Why is this important? Use an example from the text to support your answer.

.......................................................................................................................................................

.......................................................................................................................................................

---

### *Dramatic, iron-y — yep, that's the Eiffel Tower alright...*

Shakespeare's use of dramatic irony is linked to the theme of deception. The audience knows the truth throughout the play, so it's obvious when characters are being deceived or have fallen for a trick.

Page 42

# Mood and Atmosphere

**Q1** Read Act 1, Scene 3 from line 39 to the end of the scene. How does the dialogue in this passage affect the mood of the play? Explain your answer.

........................................................................................................................................

........................................................................................................................................

**Q2** Describe the atmosphere that Shakespeare creates in each of the settings below, then explain how the atmosphere is created.

**a)** The orchard (Act 3, Scene 1): ....................................................

........................................................................................................................................

........................................................................................................................................

**b)** Hero's tomb (Act 5, Scene 3): .................................................................................

........................................................................................................................................

**Q3** Why might Balthasar's song in Act 2, Scene 3 darken the mood of this scene? Explain your answer.

........................................................................................................................................

........................................................................................................................................

**Q4** Explain what mood is created by each of the quotes below.

**a)** "O God, that I were a man! I would eat his heart in the market-place."
(Act 4, Scene 1, lines 304-305)

........................................................................................................................................

........................................................................................................................................

**b)** "I have drunk poison whiles he uttered it."
(Act 5, Scene 1, line 243)

........................................................................................................................................

........................................................................................................................................

---

*I'm not in the mood to make jokes...*

Imagine you've just attended the wedding in Act 4, Scene 1. Write a short diary entry describing the atmosphere at the wedding before Hero was accused and how the atmosphere changed afterwards.

Section Four — Shakespeare's Techniques

# Poetry and Prose

**Q1** Read the following statements about poetry and prose in the play. Decide whether each statement is **true** or **false**.

| | True | False |
|---|---|---|
| *Much Ado About Nothing* is mostly written in blank verse. | ☐ | ☐ |
| The noble characters use a mix of verse and prose. | ☐ | ☐ |
| The lower-status characters mostly speak in rhyming verse. | ☐ | ☐ |
| Verse makes the characters' speech sound formal. | ☐ | ☐ |
| The play's soliloquies are all written in blank verse. | ☐ | ☐ |

Blank verse is a type of poetry. Its lines have 10 or 11 syllables, 5 main beats and they don't usually rhyme.

**Q2** Find one quote from Act 5, Scene 4 which is written in:

**a)** Prose ....................................................................................................................................

..........................................................................................................................................................

**b)** Unrhymed blank verse ..........................................................................................................

..........................................................................................................................................................

**c)** Rhyming verse ........................................................................................................................

..........................................................................................................................................................

**Q3** Read Act 1, Scene 1, lines 96-107. Why do you think that Shakespeare wrote this passage in prose? Explain your answer.

..........................................................................................................................................................

..........................................................................................................................................................

..........................................................................................................................................................

**Q4** Read Act 5, Scene 3. How does Shakespeare's use of rhyming verse contribute to the sense of tragedy in this passage? Use a quote to support your answer.

..........................................................................................................................................................

..........................................................................................................................................................

..........................................................................................................................................................

..........................................................................................................................................................

**Section Four — Shakespeare's Techniques**

**Q5**  Read Act 5, Scene 1, lines 58-71.  Why do you think these lines
are written in blank verse rather than prose?  Explain your answer.

.......................................................................................................................................

.......................................................................................................................................

.......................................................................................................................................

**Q6**  Read Act 4, Scene 1, lines 265-285.  Why do you think Shakespeare uses prose
when Benedick and Beatrice admit their love for each other?  Explain your answer.

.......................................................................................................................................

.......................................................................................................................................

.......................................................................................................................................

**Q7**  Read Act 1, Scene 1, lines 278-287.  How does
Claudio's use of blank verse in this passage make him
seem romantic?  Use a quote to support your answer.

...........................................................................

...........................................................................

...........................................................................

...........................................................................

© Sam Goldwyn/Renaissance/BBC/Kobal/REX/Shutterstock

**Q8**  Read Benedick's soliloquy in Act 2, Scene 1, lines 195-203, then answer the questions below.

**a)**  What does the soliloquy reveal about Benedick?  Use an example to support your answer.

.......................................................................................................................................

.......................................................................................................................................

**b)**  Soliloquies allow characters to express their true feelings.  How does Benedick's soliloquy
suggest that he doesn't feel comfortable talking about his feelings?  Explain your answer.

.......................................................................................................................................

.......................................................................................................................................

---

*Claudio and Hero are prose at speaking in verse...*

PRACTICE TASK

Find two examples of times in the play when Shakespeare switches from writing in prose to writing
in blank verse.  For each example, write a couple of lines to explain what effect this change has.

**Section Four — Shakespeare's Techniques**

# Imagery and Symbolism

**Q1** Read Act 3, Scene 1, lines 100-106. Find two examples of hunting imagery in this passage.

1) .........................................................................................................................................................................

2) .........................................................................................................................................................................

**Q2** Read Act 1, Scene 1, lines 55-58. Why do you think Shakespeare uses war-like imagery to describe Benedick and Beatrice's relationship? Explain your answer.

.........................................................................................................................................................................

.........................................................................................................................................................................

.........................................................................................................................................................................

**Q3** Look at the examples of imagery in the table below. For each one, identify whether it is an example of a simile, a metaphor or personification and explain the effect it has.

| Example | Type of imagery | Effect |
|---|---|---|
| a) **"I will in the interim undertake one of Hercules' labours"** (Act 2, Scene 1, lines 351-352) | | |
| b) **"let Benedick, like covered fire, / Consume away in sighs"** (Act 3, Scene 1, lines 77-78) | | |
| c) **"And so dies my revenge"** (Act 5, Scene 1, line 289) | | |

**Q4** When talking about Benedick in Act 1, Scene 1, Beatrice says "**He wears his faith but as the fashion of his hat — it ever changes with the next block.**" Explain what the clothing in this description symbolises.

.........................................................................................................................................................................

.........................................................................................................................................................................

.........................................................................................................................................................................

---

 *I wonder whether Benedick prefers a top hat or a beret...*

Some types of imagery in the play are linked to key themes. For example, Shakespeare uses hunting imagery in Act 2 and Act 3 to emphasise Benedick and Beatrice have been fooled by the deceptions.

---

# Puns and Wordplay

**Q1** Read the paragraph below and fill in the gaps using the words in the box.

A pun is sometimes formed when a word has more than one ...................................

or when two words are ................................... in the same way.  Puns are usually

..................................., so Shakespeare often uses them to create ................................... .

| conflict   shouted   humour   pronounced   emotional   funny   sad   insult   meaning |

**Q2** While discussing Don Pedro in Act 1, Scene 3, Don John says he would "**rather be a canker in a hedge than a rose in his grace**" (lines 25-26).  "**canker**" can mean 'disease' or 'rot', and it is also a type of weed.  What is the effect of this wordplay on the audience?  Explain your answer.

.................................................................................................................................

.................................................................................................................................

.................................................................................................................................

**Q3** Why are jokes about cuckolds important to the play?  Explain your answer.

© Alastair Muir/REX/Shutterstock

.................................................................................................

.................................................................................................

.................................................................................................

.................................................................................................

.................................................................................................

**Q4** Dogberry often uses the wrong words.  In Act 4, Scene 2, he says "**redemption**" (line 56) when he means 'damnation'.  Explain how this mistake creates humour.

.................................................................................................................................

.................................................................................................................................

.................................................................................................................................

---

*EXAM TIP*

***Try to spot the fantastically witty pun on the next page...***

When you're writing about Shakespeare's use of language in the exam, it's a good idea to pick out specific examples of language techniques and explain the effect that they have on the audience.

# Other Language Techniques

**Q1** In Act 4, Scene 1, the Friar says to Hero **"Come, lady, die to live."** (line 252). Answer the following questions about antithesis.

> Antithesis is a literary device where two contrasting ideas are put together.

   **a)** How does Shakespeare create antithesis in this line? Explain your answer.

   .....................................................................................................................................................

   **b)** Why do you think Shakespeare uses this contrast at this point in the play?

   .....................................................................................................................................................

   .....................................................................................................................................................

**Q2** Read Act 1, Scene 1, lines 136-150. How does Shakespeare present Don John and Don Pedro as opposites in this passage? Use an example to support your answer.

   .....................................................................................................................................................

   .....................................................................................................................................................

   .....................................................................................................................................................

   .....................................................................................................................................................

**Q3** In Act 2, Scene 2, Borachio suggests his plan **"to misuse the prince, to vex Claudio, to undo Hero and kill Leonato"**. Explain why Shakespeare might have chosen to use a list in these lines.

   .....................................................................................................................................................

**Q4** Read the examples below, then explain the effect of the repetition in each one.

   **a)** **"Foul words is but foul wind, and foul wind is but foul breath"** (Act 5, Scene 2, lines 51-52)

   .....................................................................................................................................................

   .....................................................................................................................................................

   **b)** **"The former Hero! Hero that is dead!"** (Act 5, Scene 4, line 65)

   .....................................................................................................................................................

   .....................................................................................................................................................

---

### I know tons of foul words — chicken, duck, goose, turkey...

Read Act 5, Scene 4, lines 99-127. **How are attitudes towards betrayal presented in** *Much Ado About Nothing*? You should consider:
* how Shakespeare presents attitudes towards betrayal in this extract
* how Shakespeare presents attitudes towards betrayal in the play as a whole.

# Working with Extracts

In the exam, there will be a question that asks you to write about an extract. Examiners love extract questions as they demonstrate your ability to discuss a short passage in detail. They're also a great opportunity for you to really focus on language analysis, showing that you understand how language creates meaning. This page will help you to develop the skills needed to ace any extract question.

| **Claudio:** | O Hero, what a Hero hadst thou been, |
| | If half thy outward graces had been placed |
| | About thy thoughts and counsels of thy heart! |
| | But fare thee well, most foul, most fair!  Farewell, |
| | Thou pure impiety and impious purity! |
| | For thee I'll lock up all the gates of love, |
| | And on my eyelids shall conjecture hang, |
| | To turn all beauty into thoughts of harm, |
| | And never shall it more be gracious. |
| **Leonato:** | Hath no man's dagger here a point for me? |
| | HERO *swoons* |
| **Beatrice:** | Why, how now, cousin!  Wherefore sink you down? |
| **Don John:** | Come, let us go.  These things, come thus to light, |
| | Smother her spirits up. |
| | *Exeunt* DON PEDRO, DON JOHN *and* CLAUDIO |

(Act 4, Scene 1, lines 99-111)

**Q1** Read through the extract above.  Describe what has just happened in the play before this extract and what is about to happen after it.

..............................................................................................................................

..............................................................................................................................

**Q2** Underline an example of a metaphor in the extract above.

**Q3** Claudio uses oxymorons when describing Hero in this extract.  What effect does this have?

*An oxymoron is a literary device where two contrasting terms appear together.*

..............................................................................................................................

..............................................................................................................................

**Q4** In this passage, Claudio believes that Hero has been unfaithful.  Find a second example from elsewhere in the play of Claudio believing a rumour about another character.

..............................................................................................................................

..............................................................................................................................

Section Four — Shakespeare's Techniques

# Practice Questions

*Now that you're an expert on everything from imagery to irony, it's time for another lovely set of exam-style questions. When you're writing, try to put the information from this section into practice and refer to the techniques you've learnt about. Make sure you write about form, structure and language in your answers.*

**Q1** Read the extract below from Act 5, Scene 3, then answer the following questions.

**a)** How does Shakespeare create a sombre atmosphere in this extract?
Refer only to the extract in your answer.

| | |
|---|---|
| **Claudio:** | Is this the monument of Leonato? |
| **Lord:** | It is, my lord. |
| **Claudio:** | *(Reading out of a scroll)* |
| | Done to death by slanderous tongues |
| | Was the Hero that here lies. |
| | Death, in guerdon of her wrongs, |
| | Gives her fame which never dies. |
| | So the life that died with shame |
| | Lives in death with glorious fame. |
| | *(Hangs up the scroll)* |
| | Hang thou there upon the tomb, |
| | Praising her when I am dumb. |
| | Now, music, sound, and sing your solemn hymn. |
| **Balthasar:** | *(Sings)* Pardon, goddess of the night, |
| | *Those that slew thy virgin knight;* |
| | *For the which, with songs of woe,* |
| | *Round about her tomb they go.* |
| | *Midnight, assist our moan,* |
| | *Help us to sigh and groan* |
| | *Heavily, heavily.* |
| | *Graves, yawn and yield your dead,* |
| | *Till death be uttered* |
| | *Heavily, heavily.* |
| **Claudio:** | Now, unto thy bones good night! |
| | Yearly will I do this rite. |

*(Act 5, Scene 3, lines 1-23)*

**b)** Discuss how Shakespeare presents the relationship
between Beatrice and Hero in the play.

**Q2** Read Act 5, Scene 4, lines 72-97. Explore the way Shakespeare
presents love in this extract and in the play as a whole.

**Q3** Read Act 2, Scene 3, lines 98-126. How is deception presented
in *Much Ado About Nothing*? You should consider:

- how deception is presented in this extract
- how deception is presented in the play as a whole.

**Q4** Read Act 5, Scene 1, lines 110-149. Explore the way Shakespeare
presents Benedick in this extract and in the rest of the play.

**Section Four — Shakespeare's Techniques**

# Section Five — Exam Buster

## Understanding the Question

### Underline key words in the question

**Q1** Underline the most important words in the following questions.
The first one has been done for you.

a) <u>To what extent</u> is <u>Don Pedro</u> <u>presented</u> as <u>loyal</u> in the play?

b) Write about the significance of Don John in the play.

c) Explain how the relationship between Claudio and Hero is presented.

d) Write about the importance of disloyalty in *Much Ado About Nothing*.

e) How does Shakespeare use Hero to explore the theme of reputation?

f) How is the theme of gender presented in *Much Ado About Nothing*?

g) Explain how Shakespeare presents Leonato in *Much Ado About Nothing*.

### Make sure you understand exam language

**Q2** Match each exam question to the correct explanation of what you would
need to do to answer it. You'll only need to use each white box once.

| | |
|---|---|
| **a)** To what extent is Don Pedro presented as loyal in the play? | **1)** Analyse how a theme contributes to the action of the play. |
| **b)** Write about the significance of Don John in the play. | **2)** Analyse how far a judgement or description is correct. |
| **c)** Write about the importance of disloyalty in *Much Ado About Nothing*. | **3)** Analyse how Shakespeare writes about a theme in the play. |
| **d)** How is the theme of gender presented in *Much Ado About Nothing*? | **4)** Analyse how a character contributes to the action and overall message of the play. |
| **e)** Explain how the relationship between Claudio and Hero is presented. | **5)** Analyse how characters interact and impact on each other. |

---

### *Write about the importance of ice cream during exam season...*

When you're told to start your exam, it's hard not to just dive in and write as much as you can. But this won't
help you get a good grade — firstly, read the question several times and consider what it's really asking you.

# Making a Rough Plan

## Jot down your main ideas

**Q1** Look at the exam question below, then complete the spider diagram with at least three more main points for answering it.

*Don't forget to underline the key words in the question before you start.*

Shakespeare uses Benedick's attitude towards marriage to suggest that it can be restrictive.

Read Act 1, Scene 1 from line 224 to line 252. How does Shakespeare explore ideas about marriage in this extract and in the play as a whole?

## Put your main points and examples in a logical order

**Q2** Choose your three main points from Q1 and fill in the plan below, adding evidence (a quote or an example from the text) for each point.

*One or two of your points should be about the extract from Q1.*

(Introduction)

Point One: ......................................................................................................................

Evidence: .........................................................................................................................

Point Two: .......................................................................................................................

Evidence: .........................................................................................................................

Point Three: .....................................................................................................................

Evidence: .........................................................................................................................

(Conclusion)

---

### *I bet costume designers are great at making ruff plans...*

In the exam, it's really important that you make a plan before you start writing each answer. Plans help you to stay focused and help you to stick to the most relevant points. And they should only take around 5 minutes...

**Section Five — Exam Buster**

# Making Links

## Make links with other parts of the text

**Q1** Look at the exam question and the table below. Complete the table with other relevant parts of the text which could be used to back up each point.

> Explain how Shakespeare presents Don John in *Much Ado About Nothing*.

| Point | Example 1 | Example 2 |
|---|---|---|
| Don John is disliked by the other characters. | Don John knows he is **"disdained of all"**. | |
| Don John is presented as disloyal. | He **"stood out against"** Don Pedro in the war. | |
| Don John is shown to be influential. | He pays Borachio and Conrade to help him destroy Hero's reputation. | |

## Extend your essay with other examples

*You won't have time to do really detailed planning in the exam, so you should get into the habit of thinking of links when you're doing practice questions.*

**Q2** Take each of your points from the plan you made in Q2 on p.51, and write down another example from elsewhere in the text that you could include in your essay.

Example for Point One: ................................................................................................................

........................................................................................................................................

Example for Point Two: ................................................................................................................

........................................................................................................................................

Example for Point Three: ................................................................................................................

........................................................................................................................................

---

### *Baking Link #1 — biscuits are known to increase productivity...*

To show the examiner you have a solid understanding of the play, you have to be able to make links — this makes your answers more persuasive. Try noting down any links that you come across while reading the text.

# Structuring Your Answer

## P.E.E.D. stands for Point, Example, Explain, Develop

**Q1** Read the following extract from an exam answer. Label each aspect of P.E.E.D.

> Shakespeare uses Leonato to highlight the importance of a good reputation. In Act 4, Scene 1, Leonato says "Death is the fairest cover" for Hero's "shame". This shows that Leonato believes it is better for his own child to be dead than to live in dishonour, which suggests that he views Hero's loss of reputation as an extremely serious setback that cannot be reversed. Leonato's attitude reflects the 16th-century belief that honour and a good reputation were worth dying for.

## Embedding quotes is a great way to give evidence

**Q2** Rewrite the following sentences so that a short part of the quote is embedded in each one.

**a)** Leonato says Beatrice has feelings for Benedick — **"she loves him with an enraged affection"**.

......................................................................................................................................

**b)** Claudio suggests Hero has damaged her reputation — **"Hero itself can blot out Hero's virtue"**.

......................................................................................................................................

## Structure your answer using the P.E.E.D. method

**Q3** Use the P.E.E.D. method to structure a paragraph on your first point from Q2 on page 51.

Point: ..............................................................................................................................

......................................................................................................................................

Example: ..........................................................................................................................

......................................................................................................................................

Explain: ............................................................................................................................

......................................................................................................................................

Develop: ...........................................................................................................................

......................................................................................................................................

---

### *[Insert obvious joke here]...*

You should always use the P.E.E.D. structure in your exam as it helps to make your answers brilliantly clear and concise. A good way to remember the structure is to come up with a funny joke about it — the ruder the better.

# Introductions and Conclusions

## Give a clear answer to the question in your introduction

**Q1**    Read the introductions below, then decide which is better.  Explain your choice.

> How does Shakespeare create a light-hearted mood in *Much Ado About Nothing*?

**a)**

*Much Ado About Nothing* has a largely light-hearted atmosphere throughout. Shakespeare mostly uses prose instead of blank verse.  This creates a light-hearted mood by making the atmosphere on stage feel less formal. It also increases the pace of the characters' witty exchanges, creating more humour for the audience.

**b)**

Shakespeare uses several techniques to create a light-hearted mood for the audience.  His use of wordplay and puns creates humour, and the witty exchanges between Beatrice and Benedick add to the play's light-hearted atmosphere.  The play is also mostly in prose, which creates an informal mood on stage.

Better Intro: ...................................    Reason:  .............................................................

...........................................................................................................................

...........................................................................................................................

...........................................................................................................................

## Don't write any new points in your conclusion

**Q2**    Read this conclusion to the exam question in Q1, then explain how it could be improved.

> In conclusion, Shakespeare creates a light-hearted mood in *Much Ado About Nothing* by skilfully integrating puns and wordplay.  Benedick and Beatrice often use puns in their speech, which shows that they are both very witty and intelligent characters.

...........................................................................................................................

...........................................................................................................................

...........................................................................................................................

...........................................................................................................................

...........................................................................................................................

---

### *I'm a slow writer — I never manage to finish my conclusio...*

Write an introduction and conclusion for the exam question on page 51.  Keep in mind the good and bad examples on this page and make sure you always make the introduction and conclusion relevant to the question.

---

# Writing about Context

## Make sure you can link the play to its context

**Q1**  Match each statement with the relevant contextual information.

**a)** Leonato commands Hero to answer truthfully when Claudio questions her at the wedding.

**b)** Leonato is happy for Hero to marry a count like Claudio.

**c)** Benedick challenges Claudio to a duel after Claudio shames Hero and damages her reputation.

**1)** Many nobles in the 16th century believed it was important to marry someone with the same social status.

**2)** People valued honour very highly in the 16th century, so they were often willing to die to protect it.

**3)** In the 16th century, children were expected to obey the wishes of their father.

## Include context in your answer

**Q2**  Read the sample answer below and underline the contextual information.

> Don John's character reflects the difficulties that illegitimate children faced in the 16th century. In Act 1, Scene 3, Conrade says Don John should not reveal his villainous nature because he has only "newly" been taken into Don Pedro's "grace". This shows that Don John is reliant on Don Pedro's favour, reflecting that illegitimate children in the 16th century had no rights to their father's inheritance and had less power in society than their siblings. Shakespeare uses language related to imprisonment, such as "muzzle" and "cage", to show that Don John feels constrained by his reliance on his brother.

**Q3**  Now write a paragraph using either your second or third point from page 51.
You should include contextual information and use the P.E.E.D. method.

..................................................................................................................................................

..................................................................................................................................................

..................................................................................................................................................

..................................................................................................................................................

..................................................................................................................................................

..................................................................................................................................................

---

### *Context — L__k wha_ happ__s wh__ y_u l_av_ i_ _u_ ...*

In the exam, you need to show the examiner that you understand the relationship between the play and its context. There are loads of ways you can do this, just make sure your context is always relevant to the point you're making.

# Linking Ideas and Paragraphs

## Link your ideas so your argument is easy to follow

**Q1**   Rewrite the sample answer below so that the ideas are clearly linked.

> Borachio is presented as manipulative.  In Act 5, Scene 1, he confesses that Don John "incensed" him to "slander" Hero.  In Act 1, Scene 3, it is Borachio who devises the plan to damage Hero's reputation.  Borachio is willing to lie to make himself seem less guilty.  It is easy for the audience to see him as one of the villains of the play.

..................................................................................................................................

..................................................................................................................................

..................................................................................................................................

..................................................................................................................................

..................................................................................................................................

**Q2**   Write a paragraph using your third point from p.51.  Make sure your ideas are properly linked.

..................................................................................................................................

..................................................................................................................................

..................................................................................................................................

..................................................................................................................................

..................................................................................................................................

## Show how your paragraphs follow on from each other

**Q3**   Look at the paragraphs you have written on p.53, p.55 and on this page using your points from p.51.  Write down linking words or phrases you could use to link them together in your answer.

| Paragraphs to link | Linking word or phrase |
|---|---|
| Points 1 and 2 | |
| Points 2 and 3 | |

## *Paragraphs should be like Beatrice — sharp and to the point...*

Read the question carefully and make a plan before you write your answer.  If you know what you want to argue before you start writing, then the links between your ideas will be a lot clearer.  And remember to use P.E.E.D.

# Marking Answer Extracts

## Get familiar with the mark scheme

| Grade band | An answer at this level... |
|---|---|
| 8-9 | • shows an insightful and critical personal response to the text<br>• closely and perceptively analyses how the writer uses language, form and structure to create meaning and affect the reader, making use of highly relevant subject terminology<br>• supports arguments with well-integrated, highly relevant and precise examples from the text<br>• gives a detailed exploration of the relationship between the text and its context<br>• uses highly varied vocabulary and sentence types, with mostly accurate spelling and punctuation |
| 6-7 | • shows a critical and observant personal response to the text<br>• includes a thorough exploration of how the writer uses language, form and structure to create meaning and affect the reader, making use of appropriate subject terminology<br>• supports arguments with integrated, well-chosen examples from the text<br>• explores the relationship between the text and its context<br>• uses a substantial range of vocabulary and sentence types, with generally accurate spelling and punctuation |
| 4-5 | • shows a thoughtful and clear personal response to the text<br>• examines how the writer uses language, form and structure to create meaning and affect the reader, making some use of relevant subject terminology<br>• integrates appropriate examples from the text<br>• shows an understanding of contextual factors<br>• uses a moderate range of vocabulary and sentence types, without spelling and punctuation errors which make the meaning unclear |

## Have a go at marking an answer extract

**Q1** Using the mark scheme, put the sample answer extract below in a grade band and explain why.

> How is Don Pedro presented as a respectable character in *Much Ado About Nothing*?

> Don Pedro is shown to be a respectable character through the way other characters treat him. Leonato asks Don Pedro if it will "Please" him to "lead on" into the house. This polite behaviour suggests Leonato wants to show respect to Don Pedro. After this, Don Pedro asks for Leonato's hand and insists on them entring the house "together", which shows he respects Leonato too.

Grade Band: ............................ Reason: ...........................................................

........................................................................................................................

........................................................................................................................

........................................................................................................................

# Marking Answer Extracts

## Have a look at these extracts from answers to the question on p.57

**Q1**  For each extract, say what grade band you think it is in, then underline an example of where it meets each of the mark scheme criteria.  Label each underlined point to show what it achieves.

---

**a)**  Shakespeare presents Don Pedro as respectable by opening the play with a discussion of his victory in battle.  The Messenger emphasises how impressive Don Pedro's recent victory is by describing how he "brings home full numbers", highlighting how few of his men died.  As noblemen in the 16th century followed a code of honour influenced by medieval chivalry, presenting Don Pedro as a good soldier frames him as a knightly hero in the eyes of the audience, making him seem honourable and worthy of respect before he has even appeared on stage.  Furthermore, when Don Pedro does appear, his first lines of dialogue are politely addressed to Leonato, who he praises as a noble and gracious host.  This confirms the audience's impression that Don Pedro is respectable by showing that his courteous actions match his impressive reputation.

Don Pedro is also presented as respectable through his status as a prince.  He is referred to as "my lord", "your grace", "My liege" and "Sweet Prince" by various other characters.  The word "grace", which is associated with God, links Don Pedro to the 16th-century belief that noblemen were more virtuous than people of lower social status and therefore more deserving of respect.  The repetition of these titles throughout the play highlights the respect that is consistently shown to Don Pedro by other characters.  Don Pedro is also shown to be respectable through the extent to which other characters respect his status as a prince.  In Act 1, Scene 1, Leonato welcomes Don John because Don John has been forgiven by "the Prince".  This highlights the power of Leonato's respect for Don Pedro, as it shows that he extends hospitality to Don John because of his association with Don Pedro.

---

Grade Band: ................................

---

**b)**  Don Pedro's respectability is demonstrated when he apologises for his role in dishonouring Hero.  He vows to "bend under any heavy weight" that Leonato desires.  This emphasises the sincerity of Don Pedro's apology, as he is willing to atone for his error even though the word "heavy" implies that he expects his punishment to be severe.  The fact that Don Pedro overlooks social hierarchies and allows himself to be punished by Leonato, a man of inferior social status, shows that Don Pedro does not use his high status to his advantage.  This goes against the 16th-century belief in the importance of maintaining the strict social order, so the fact that Don Pedro cares more about earning Leonato's forgiveness than following society's expectations suggests that he is a noble and respectable character.

The contrast between Don Pedro and Don John's behaviour emphasises that Don Pedro is a more respected character than his brother.  For example, the structure of Act 2, Scene 1, highlights just how different they are.  First, Don Pedro selflessly attempts to woo Hero for Claudio, then immediately afterwards Don John lies to Claudio to try and ruin his relationship with Hero.  The stark contrast between their actions emphasises how much more worthy of respect Don Pedro is than his brother, as Don Pedro tries to help the other characters and Don John tries to cause trouble for them.  Don Pedro's desire to help his friends also demonstrates his respectability by linking him to the theme of loyalty, as he keeps his promise to woo Hero from Act 1, Scene 1.  Shakespeare continues presenting Don Pedro as honourable and loyal throughout the play, which encourages the audience to view him as a respectable character.

---

Grade Band: ................................

---

# Marking a Whole Answer

Now try marking this whole answer

**Q1**   Read the sample answer below.  On page 60, put it in a grade band and explain your decision.

Read Act 1, Scene 1, lines 108-135.  Explain how the relationship between Benedick and Beatrice is important in *Much Ado About Nothing*.  You should write about the extract and the play as a whole.

If it helps you, label examples of where the answer meets the mark scheme criteria.

Beatrice and Benedick's relationship in the play reveals important information about their characters and attitudes.  The couple's verbal sparring also provides humour and sets a comedic tone.  Furthermore, their relationship plays a key role in the exploration of the play's central themes.  Misunderstandings between the two eventual lovers allow Shakespeare to examine ideas about deception, while the development of the couple's relationship highlights the powerful effects of love and the politics of marriage which drive the play.

The relationship between Beatrice and Benedick plays a key role in illustrating Beatrice's independent nature.  In the extract, Beatrice is outspoken in her dislike of Benedick, telling him "Nobody marks you" and that he could turn courtesy "to disdain".  This shows that Beatrice is unusually outspoken, as women in the 16th century were expected to be quiet, demure and obedient rather than being as vocal, witty and critical as Beatrice is.  The word "disdain" also implies that Beatrice considers Benedick unworthy of her, which shows that she has a strong sense of self-worth, despite the fact that 16th-century society determined the value of women by their relationships with men.  However, there is a hint in Act 5 that Beatrice will be changed by her marriage to Benedick.  Though she is still arguing with him, he says "Peace!  I will stop your mouth", which reflects that, as her husband, he will have the authority to limit her independence.

Benedick's relationship with Beatrice also causes his character to undergo important changes over the course of the play.  Benedick's attitude to marriage changes once he realises that he is in love with Beatrice.  In the extract, which comes from the beginning of the play, Benedick says "I love none", despite being "loved of all ladies".  However, by Act 5, he has resolved to marry Beatrice and vows to "live in thy heart, die in thy lap and be buried in thy eyes".  The repetition of "thy" in this vow shows that Benedick no longer thinks only of himself and that he is willing to commit himself to Beatrice entirely, while the references to death imply he intends to be faithful for the rest of his life.  Furthermore, at the end of the play, Benedick implores Don Pedro to "get thee a wife!"  This radical change in Benedick's attitude to love and marriage shows how powerful love is, because it has completely changed his outlook on life.

Beatrice and Benedick's exchanges are also an important source of comedy in the play.  In the extract, Shakespeare uses their quarrelling to create humour for the audience.  The pair insult each other freely, with Beatrice telling Benedick that "Scratching" his face could not make it less attractive, prompting Benedick to respond by calling Beatrice a "rare parrot-teacher".  This back and forth of witty retorts engages the audience as they laugh at the escalating insults and wait to see which character will win the verbal duel.  Beatrice and Benedick's exchanges are also important to the play's form as a comedy.  By presenting Beatrice and Benedick's relationship as comedic rather than traditionally romantic in the first act, Shakespeare immediately shows the audience that they are an unconventional couple who will not be involved in a typical courtly romance.

Elsewhere in the play, Shakespeare uses the misunderstandings between Beatrice and Benedick to create more humour for the audience.  For example, Benedick's behaviour after he has been tricked in Act 2 adds further comedy to the play.  In Act 2, Scene 3, Benedick's declaration that he can "spy some marks of love" in Beatrice is juxtaposed with Beatrice's coldness when she invites Benedick to dinner "Against" her "will".  This creates humour through dramatic irony, as the audience knows that Benedick has misunderstood Beatrice's

This answer continues on p.60. ⟶

# Marking a Whole Answer

behaviour and can enjoy watching him behave as though his misguided opinion is true. Misunderstandings also entertain the audience in Act 5, Scene 4, when Beatrice and Benedick realise they have both been misled. Shakespeare structures their dialogue so that the two characters echo each other, repeating the phrase "They swore that you were...". This mirroring highlights the pair's simultaneous realisation that they were originally brought together by lies. It is humorous for the audience to watch the couple publicly admit their feelings for each other at the same time as they discover their relationship was built on misunderstandings.

Shakespeare uses Beatrice and Benedick's misunderstandings about each other's feelings to explore the theme of deception in the play. The development of Beatrice and Benedick's relationship is used to show that some forms of deception can be a force for good. The play is structured so that the pair are tricked in quick succession, with Benedick being deceived first in Act 2, Scene 3, and then Beatrice in Act 3, Scene 1. Structuring the play like this suggests that the tricks happen swiftly, which highlights how easy it is to convince the pair that they really care about each other. This suggests that their feelings of love already existed, which makes their friends' decision to deceive them seem favourable because it helps the couple to recognise their feelings. An Elizabethan audience might have viewed the deceptions as especially helpful to Benedick and Beatrice. It was a strongly-held belief in the 16th century that men and women should get married, so Shakespeare's audience would have seen Benedick and Beatrice overcoming their dislike of marriage as a very positive outcome.

In addition, Beatrice and Benedick's relationship plays an important role in Shakespeare's exploration of the theme of love and marriage in the play. Shakespeare uses language to create a contrast between their relationship and that of Claudio and Hero, which emphasises that there are different kinds of romance. For example, Hero and Claudio often use blank verse to discuss their relationship. Blank verse is an unnatural kind of speech, which emphasises the artificial and slightly surreal nature of Hero and Claudio's courtly love. In contrast, Beatrice and Benedick often speak in prose, which makes their more unconventional relationship seem practical and real, as prose is more like natural speech. Shakespeare also highlights Benedick and Beatrice's unusual approach to romance when they say that they "suffer love" for each other. This oxymoron contrasts the traditionally positive qualities of love with the verb "suffer", which suggests an experience of something unpleasant or even painful. This shows that Benedick and Beatrice are not traditionally romantic or sentimental about love.

In conclusion, it is clear that Beatrice and Benedick's relationship is a crucial part of *Much Ado About Nothing*. Their interactions throughout the play provide the audience with an insight into their characters and how they change during the play. Their relationship is a key source of comedy and ultimately contributes towards the play's happy conclusion. Furthermore, the way their unconventional romance is used to explore the key themes of deception and love demonstrates how important their romance is to the plot.

Grade Band: ....................................    Reasons: ........................................................................................

........................................................................................................................................................

........................................................................................................................................................

........................................................................................................................................................

........................................................................................................................................................

........................................................................................................................................................

---

## *Poor Mark — he's always being judged...*

Knowing what you need to do to get a good mark in the exam is really important. If you practise including things like language analysis, structure and context now, it'll be second nature by the time you do the exam.

# Writing Well

It might seem obvious, but it's important that you use the correct spelling, punctuation and grammar (SPaG for short) in your exam.  5% of the marks in your English Literature GCSE are for writing well, which includes using a wide range of vocabulary, technical terms and sentence structures, as well as accurate SPaG.  It's best if you leave yourself a few minutes at the end of the exam to check over your work and correct any mistakes.  If you see one, draw a line through it and put your correction above.

**Q1**  Read the sample answer below.  Underline all of the SPaG mistakes, then correct them.
One has already been done for you.

> *Benedick's*
> At the start of the play, <u>Benedict's</u> disapproval of marrage is used to create humour.  He worried
>
> that he will not "see a bachelor of three-score' again after Claudio confesses his desire to marry
>
> hero.  The phrase "of three-score" means sixty years old.  Most men in Shakespeares time would
>
> have married by this age: which makes Benedick's opinion seem slightly ridiculus.

**Q2**  Match each technical term to the correct example.
You'll only need to use each example once.

| | |
|---|---|
| **a)** Metaphor | **1)** "For a hawk, a horse, or a husband?" |
| **b)** Simile | **2)** "For look where Beatrice, like a lapwing, runs" |
| **c)** Repetition | **3)** "There is a kind of merry war betwixt Signior Benedick and her" |
| **d)** Oxymoron | **4)** "war-thoughts / Have left their places vacant" |
| **e)** Alliteration | **5)** "O, she is fallen / Into a pit of ink" |
| **f)** Personification | **6)** "But, for my will, my will is your good will" |

# Practice Questions

*Now you know how to write great exam answers, it would be rude not to give you some practice questions to test your skills out on. I know... I'm too good to you. Have a go at doing these questions under exam conditions — turn off your music, find a quiet spot and give yourself about 45 minutes on each question.*

**Q1** Read the extract below from Act 1, Scene 1. To what extent does Shakespeare present Beatrice as intelligent? Refer to this extract and to the play as a whole.

| | |
|---|---|
| **Leonato:** | You must not, sir, mistake my niece. There is a kind of merry war betwixt Signior Benedick and her: they never meet but there's a skirmish of wit between them. |
| **Beatrice:** | Alas, he gets nothing by that. In our last conflict four of his five wits went halting off, and now is the whole man governed with one, so that if he have wit enough to keep himself warm, let him bear it for a difference between himself and his horse, for it is all the wealth that he hath left, to be known a reasonable creature. Who is his companion now? He hath every month a new sworn brother. |
| **Messenger:** | Is't possible? |
| **Beatrice:** | Very easily possible. He wears his faith but as the fashion of his hat — it ever changes with the next block. |
| **Messenger:** | I see, lady, the gentleman is not in your books. |
| **Beatrice:** | No — an he were, I would burn my study. |

*(Act 1, Scene 1, lines 55-73)*

**Q2** **a)** Read Act 2, Scene 3, lines 219-246. How might the audience react to Benedick's thoughts in this extract?

**b)** Discuss times in the play when Hero may deserve sympathy.

**Q3** Read Act 5, Scene 1, lines 262-292. Explore the way Shakespeare presents Claudio in this extract and in the rest of the play.

**Q4** Read Act 3, Scene 1, lines 1-25, then answer the following questions.

**a)** Explain how Hero is presented as confident in this extract.

**b)** In this extract, Hero begins to carry out a scheme to trick Beatrice. Write about the importance of secret schemes in the play. You should consider:
- where secret schemes appear in the play
- how secret schemes influence events in the play.

**Section Five — Exam Buster**

# Answers

## Section One — Analysis of Acts

### Page 2: Act One — Scene 1

1. The statements should be numbered 4, 5, 1, 7, 2, 3, 6.
2. a) Messenger — I see you don't approve of Benedick.
   b) Benedick — All women find me attractive.
3. a) E.g. "In mine eye she is the sweetest lady that ever I looked on." (lines 175-176)
   b) E.g. "I will live a bachelor." (lines 231-232)
4. E.g. Don Pedro is a loyal friend to Claudio because he is willing to help him woo Hero. He is happy to do anything to help Claudio, telling him "My love is thine to teach."

### Page 3: Act One — Scenes 2 and 3

1. a) False: e.g. "I can tell you strange news that you yet dreamt not of." (lines 3-4)
   b) True: e.g. "We will hold it as a dream till it appear itself". (lines 18-19)
2. E.g. He plans to tell Hero of the rumour so she is prepared to answer Don Pedro.
3. E.g. So Don John can regain his brother's favour.
4. E.g. Meaning: He would prefer to be hated than pretend to be something he is not in order to be liked. Any valid explanation, e.g. Don John knows he is disliked by most people, but he doesn't care about their opinions.
5. E.g. He wants to hurt Claudio because he resents him for earning "glory" by defeating him in the war.

### Page 4: Act Two — Scene 1

1. a) E.g. "Would it not grieve a woman to be overmastered with a piece of valiant dust?" (lines 58-59)
   b) E.g. "if the Prince do solicit you in that kind, you know your answer" (lines 64-66).
   c) E.g. "The fault will be in the music, cousin, if you be not wooed in good time." (lines 67-68)
2. false, true, false, true, true, false
3. E.g. Ursula immediately sees through Antonio's disguise. / Beatrice knows she's talking to Benedick, despite his disguise.
4. E.g. He thinks it's Claudio's own fault that he lost Hero, as he drew Don Pedro's attention to her and gave him a chance to woo her for himself.

### Page 5: Act Two — Scene 1 continued and Scene 2

1. E.g. He is hurt by what she said and feels that her comments about him were too harsh.
   Quote: e.g. "she misused me past the endurance of a block!" (lines 232-233)
2. E.g. "I gave him use for it, a double heart for his single one." (lines 272-273) Any valid explanation, e.g. She might seem less cold-hearted, as she has a reason to be scornful of love.
3. E.g. Don Pedro convinces Claudio he was wooing Hero for him.
4. E.g. Claudio is so happy that he becomes speechless. He then vows that he will devote himself to Hero.
5. E.g. To create tension for the audience by introducing a threat to Claudio and Hero's new relationship.
6. E.g. Borachio will flirt with Margaret at Hero's bedroom window and make sure Claudio sees them. He will "call Margaret Hero" to persuade Claudio that he is speaking to Hero rather than Margaret.

### Page 6: Act Two — Scene 3

1. E.g. He sets impossible standards for the woman he will marry, saying she must be "virtuous", "Rich" and "fair". This suggests he will never find a suitable wife.
2. E.g. He is suggesting men can't be trusted when it comes to love, as they'll pretend to be in love even if they are not.
3. a) True: e.g. "Bait the hook well — this fish will bite." (line 115)
   b) False: e.g. "Why, it must be requited." (line 223) / "I will be horribly in love with her" (line 234).
4. E.g. He wants Hero, Ursula and Margaret to deceive Beatrice with a similar trick to the one played on Benedick.

5. E.g. Benedick thinks that Beatrice is being affectionate. This misunderstanding creates humour, as the audience knows Beatrice is actually angry with Benedick.

### Page 7: Act Three — Scene 1

1. E.g. "This is thy office — / Bear thee well in it and leave us alone." (lines 12-13) Any valid explanation, e.g. In Act 1, Hero was passive and quiet, but here she is confident and acts like a leader.
2. E.g. It suggests Hero understands Beatrice very well, as she knows exactly how to get Beatrice to come to the orchard.
3. b) E.g. Hero insults Beatrice, saying "Nature never framed a woman's heart / Of prouder stuff".
   c) E.g. Hero calls Benedick "the only man of Italy".
   d) E.g. Hero claims it would be better for Benedick to die than for Beatrice to make fun of him.
4. E.g. In Act 1, Beatrice doesn't want to fall in love. This line shows that she no longer finds romance undesirable, as she says 'goodbye' to the "Contempt" and "pride" that stopped her from falling in love with Benedick before this moment.

### Page 8: Act Three — Scenes 2 and 3

1. E.g. It shows that he intends to woo Beatrice and is serious about the vow he made in Act 2, Scene 3 to requite her love.
2. E.g. They know Benedick has mocked other people for being in love, so they want to make fun of him in return.
3. E.g. It might make him seem cruel for deciding to reject her in such a harsh and public way.
4. E.g. They accept Dogberry's ridiculous orders, such as not to arrest thieves. / They misunderstand Borachio's words and think he is talking about a criminal called "Deformed".
5. E.g. Claudio believed Margaret was Hero because it was dark and he saw her from a distance, and Borachio's "villainy" confirmed the "slander that Don John had made".

### Page 9: Act Three — Scenes 4 and 5

1. E.g. Hero is shocked by Margaret's sexual joke, saying "Fie upon thee! Art not ashamed?", which suggests that she is not used to discussing sex.
2. E.g. She feels "out of all other tune" because she is feeling love for Benedick, which is unfamiliar to her.
3. a) E.g. She compares Benedick to a medicine and suggests that Beatrice will feel better if she lets Benedick into her heart.
   b) E.g. She suggests that Beatrice is attracted to Benedick.
4. E.g. "Neighbours, you are tedious." (line 17) / "I would fain know what you have to say." (line 28)
5. E.g. He asks Dogberry to question the prisoners himself.
6. E.g. To create tension before the wedding, as it's not clear whether the Watch will be able to reveal the truth before Claudio shames Hero.

Task: Here are some points you could have included:
- The mood becomes more serious at the end of Act 3, Scene 1 when Beatrice considers her love for Benedick.
- The end of Act 3, Scene 2 is serious as Don John starts to carry out his plan to make Hero seem unfaithful. However, in Act 3, Scene 3 when Dogberry and Verges are introduced, their incompetence creates humour that lightens the mood.

### Page 10: Act Four — Scene 1

1. The statements should be numbered 1, 5, 4, 2, 3.
2. E.g. To shame Hero publicly. Going along with the wedding means that everyone's attention is focused on them when he rejects her.
3. E.g. Claudio suggests that Hero has deceived him by only pretending to be pure when she is actually unfaithful.
4. E.g. It makes him seem heartless because it suggests he doesn't care whether or not Hero will recover.
5. E.g. "O, on my soul, my cousin is belied!" (line 145)
   Any valid explanation, e.g. It suggests Beatrice has faith in Hero, as she believes she is innocent and acts to protect her.

# Answers

## Page 11: Act Four — Scene 1 continued and Scene 2

1. E.g. He is in love with Beatrice and he wants to support her because she is experiencing an upsetting situation. / Benedick suspects Don John has played a part in Hero's rejection, so he is reluctant to abandon her without questioning the accusations.

2. E.g. He thinks the news of Hero's death will shock Claudio into realising he is wrong about her. / He hopes people will grieve her instead of remembering her ruined reputation. / To give Hero's friends time to clear her name before revealing that she is alive.

3. E.g. The beginning of Benedick and Beatrice's romantic relationship creates a positive end to a tragic scene, which gives the audience hope that there will be a happy ending.

4. E.g. He takes over the questioning from Dogberry and he asks the Watch direct questions so he can get all the facts.

5. "Prince John is this morning secretly stolen away." (lines 60-61) Any valid explanation, e.g. His plan went wrong when Hero 'died', so he might have fled to avoid punishment in case people find out he is responsible.

Task: Here are some points you could have included:
- Borachio's greed leads him to encourage Don John's plotting against Claudio and Hero. It is Borachio who comes up with the plan to make Hero seem disloyal after Don John's first plan fails.
- Honour and reputation are important to Claudio. Don John's plot to make Hero seem unfaithful is successful, which leads Claudio to believe that his honour is at stake. This makes him decide to publicly shame Hero at the wedding.
- The incompetence of the Watch means that an opportunity to reveal Hero's innocence is lost before the wedding. Dogberry fails to tell Leonato about Borachio's plot, which means Leonato is unable to protect Hero from being shamed.

## Page 12: Act Five — Scene 1

1. E.g. Meaning: I don't want anyone to comfort me unless they have experienced the same things I have.
Any valid explanation, e.g. Leonato is so upset about Hero's shame that he thinks no one can understand how he feels.

2. a) E.g. "Make those that do offend you suffer too." (line 40)
b) E.g. "My soul doth tell me Hero is belied". (line 42)
c) E.g. "Away! I will not have to do with you." (line 77)

3. E.g. He is willing to risk his life to support his brother in a duel and defend their family honour, telling Leonato to let him "deal in this".

4. E.g. Claudio and Don Pedro believe that Hero is dead at this point in the play. Their light-hearted behaviour seems insensitive because the audience feels they should be showing sorrow for Hero's death instead.

## Page 13: Act Five — Scene 1 continued

1. E.g. Benedick has fallen in love, but he is acting seriously and honourably, and it is Claudio and Don Pedro who are acting like fools.

2. E.g. To avoid a harsher punishment by blaming everything on Don John. Borachio claims Don John "incensed" him to slander Hero, even though it was Borachio's idea.

3. a) E.g. His feelings for Hero return when he learns she is innocent.
b) E.g. He will do anything to make up for wronging Hero.
c) E.g. He still doesn't accept full responsibility for the way he treated Hero.

4. E.g. They were cruel to shame Hero so publicly, as they had no solid evidence of her guilt. / They didn't think about Leonato or Hero's honour when they acted to protect their own.

5. E.g. Yes, because Claudio was not fully to blame and he is given a chance to redeem himself by marrying Hero's 'cousin'. **Or** e.g. No, because Claudio still ends up marrying Hero as part of his 'punishment', even though he rejected and humiliated her.

## Page 14: Act Five — Scenes 2 and 3

1. a) E.g. They exchange witty jokes and comments, which is amusing for the audience.

b) E.g. She is suggesting that his insults aren't very effective.

2. E.g. It suggests his love for her is strong. He compares himself to classical romantic heroes but suggests even they were "never so truly turned over and over" by love as he is.

3. You should have ticked the second and third statements.

4. E.g. To resolve the tragic aspects of the plot quickly so the play can move towards its happy ending.

5. E.g. The song contains imagery relating to death, such as when he asks the graves to "yawn and yield your dead". This creates a dark tone that reinforces the tragic mood.

## Page 15: Act Five — Scene 4

1. The statements should be numbered 3, 1, 4, 2, 5.

2. a) Hero — The Hero that 'died' was disgraced, but this Hero is free from shame.
b) Benedick — The poems prove Benedick and Beatrice are in love.

3. E.g. It suggests they now accept their feelings for each other, as they no longer reject the conventions of courtly love.

4. E.g. To show how much he has changed since Act 1. At the start of the play, he made fun of people for wanting to get married, but now he is promoting marriage to Don Pedro.

5. E.g. It quickly resolves the loose ends of the plot without spoiling the play's happy ending.

Task: Here are some points you could have included:
- Act 1: e.g. Claudio falls in love with Hero / Don Pedro promises to woo Hero for Claudio / Don John plots to ruin Claudio and Hero's wedding.
- Act 2: e.g. Leonato agrees that Claudio can marry Hero / Borachio suggests a plan to make Claudio think Hero has been disloyal / Don Pedro, Claudio and Leonato make Benedick believe Beatrice loves him.
- Act 3: e.g. Hero tricks Beatrice into believing Benedick loves her / Don John tricks Claudio into believing Hero is unfaithful / Borachio and Conrade are arrested.
- Act 4: e.g. Claudio accuses Hero of being unfaithful / Friar Francis suggests Hero should pretend to be dead / Benedick and Beatrice confess their love for each other.
- Act 5: e.g. Borachio confesses to the plot, confirming Hero's innocence / Hero reveals she is alive and she and Claudio are reunited / Beatrice agrees to marry Benedick.

## Page 16: Skills Focus — Using Quotes

1. true, true, false, false, false

2. b) Don Pedro believes that being "of a noble strain" makes Benedick a suitable husband for Beatrice.
c) Hero says it will be easy to "stain" Beatrice's reputation by gossiping about her.
d) Leonato believes Hero's unfaithfulness is "stronger made" once Beatrice admits that she didn't sleep in Hero's bed.
e) Benedick writes "A halting sonnet", which suggests that he wants to woo Beatrice.

## Page 17: Skills Focus — P.E.E.D.

1. a) The Explain stage is missing.
b) The Develop stage is missing.

2. a) E.g. This implies that words can be deadly.
E.g. She compares Claudio to a bitter 'Seville orange', saying he is as "civil as an orange".

## Section Two — Characters

### Page 18: Hero

1. b) E.g. She is able to stand up for herself when she is in a position of authority.
c) E.g. She is emotionally fragile.

2. E.g. It suggests that she thinks love is unpredictable and that everyone experiences it in a different way.

3. E.g. Hero uses exclamations like "O, God defend me!", which shows her surprise. She also asks questions, which shows she can't believe that Claudio thinks she is unfaithful.

# Answers

4.  E.g. Leonato wants her to marry Claudio, so Hero has no choice. She may only forgive Claudio and marry him to please her father. / She may be in love with Claudio. In Act 3, Scene 1, she refers to him as "my dear Claudio", which suggests she cares about him, and her feelings may not have not changed.

Task: Here are some points you could have included:
- In the extract, Hero is presented as witty.
  - "God defend the lute should be like the case!"
  - Metaphor: she hopes his face ("lute") is better than his mask ("case"). Uses language cleverly.
  - Form of play = comedy. Witty jokes create humour.
- Elsewhere in the play, Hero is presented as playful.
  - Exclaims "O god of love!" when tricking Beatrice.
  - Exclamatory language: makes her seem dramatic, suggests she's enjoying the trick.
  - Shows the audience a different side to Hero compared to Act 1 — makes her a more interesting character.
- Hero is often presented as quiet and passive in the play.
  - Act 1, Scene 1: only speaks once, on stage the whole time.
  - She conforms to expectations for 16th-century women — quiet, demure, submissive to men.
  - Modern audience might react negatively — different expectations for 21st-century women.

## Page 19: Claudio

1.  true, false, true, false, false
2.  a) E.g. He thinks Claudio is arrogant and resents him for the part he played in defeating Don John in the war: e.g. "That young start-up hath all the glory of my overthrow." (lines 62-63)
    b) E.g. She thinks Claudio is a great man who is better than all other men in Italy: e.g. "He is the only man of Italy, / Always excepted my dear Claudio." (lines 92-93)
3.  E.g. Claudio believes that Don Pedro has wooed Hero "for himself", even though they are friends and he hasn't seen proof of his betrayal. / Claudio suggests that he can "trust no agent", but the audience knows that it is only Don John and Borachio who are trying to deceive him.
4.  E.g. He thinks he has been tricked into agreeing to marry a woman who has been unfaithful to him, which makes him look foolish and threatens his respectable reputation.

Task: Here are some points that you might have included:
- In Act 2, Scene 1, he is very quick to believe that Don Pedro "woos for himself", which makes the audience see him as childish and jealous.
- In Act 4, Scene 1, he seems cruel when he publicly shames Hero instead of discussing his suspicions privately.
- He mocks Leonato in Act 5, Scene 1, even though he thinks Leonato is grieving for Hero. This makes him seem heartless.

## Page 20: Beatrice

1.  assertive, rebels, wit, afraid, defying
2.  E.g. At the start of the play, she never wants to get married, but she changes her mind after she hears that Benedick loves her.
3.  E.g. It makes her seem vulnerable, as the way that she questions her past behaviour shows the audience that she cares about what people think of her.
4.  a) Hero — She judges people too harshly.
    b) Benedick — She cares deeply about Hero and is upset at her treatment.

## Page 21: Benedick

1.  a) E.g. "Thou hast frighted the word out of his right sense, so forcible is thy wit." (Act 5, Scene 2, lines 54-55)
    b) E.g. "I will do myself the right to trust none". (Act 1, Scene 1, lines 229-230)
    c) E.g. "But it is certain I am loved of all ladies". (Act 1, Scene 1, lines 115-116).
2.  E.g. Yes, because he thinks he's better than Claudio and mocks him for falling in love. **Or** e.g. No, because he's willing to see the error of his ways and changes his attitudes to love and women.

3.  E.g. It shows that he is brave and honourable, as he's willing to challenge Claudio to a duel to defend Beatrice and Hero.
4.  E.g. He starts the scene with a negative attitude to love, saying a "man is a fool" if he falls in love. He ends it with a positive attitude, looking for "marks of love" in Beatrice.

Exam Practice:
Your answer should have an introduction, several paragraphs developing different ideas and a conclusion. You may have covered some of the following points:
- Shakespeare uses Benedick's language in this extract to make him seem sensitive. When Don Pedro mentions Beatrice, Benedick uses exclamatory language, crying "O" at the start of his speech and then declaring that Beatrice has "misused" him. This emotional reaction suggests that he has taken Beatrice's criticisms to heart and emphasises how upset he feels. Shakespeare also structures Benedick's dialogue to make him seem sensitive, giving him a long speech that suggests he is so overwhelmed by emotion that he cannot stop ranting.
- In this extract, Benedick's sensitivity is shown through his reaction to Beatrice's insults. He compares her insults to daggers and says "every word stabs". The use of "stabs" suggests that Beatrice's words are so brutal and cutting to Benedick that it feels as though he is being physically injured. The fact that Beatrice's words are able to hurt Benedick so deeply highlights his sensitivity to the insults. Shakespeare's audience might have been surprised by Benedick's willingness to express how much Beatrice has hurt him, as Elizabethan men were expected to have power over women rather than the other way around.
- In the play, Shakespeare uses Benedick's soliloquies to present him as sensitive. At the end of Act 2, Benedick asks rhetorical questions, such as "doth not the appetite alter?" as he considers how his attitude to love has changed. The fact that he questions himself implies that he finds love complicated and confusing. This shows he is more sensitive to conflicts in his emotions than other characters in the play, who treat love as a purely positive force. Using Benedick's soliloquies to reveal this side of his character encourages the audience to view his emotional sensitivity as authentic, as he is alone on stage so is able to show his true self.

## Page 22: Don Pedro

1.  a) E.g. The other characters obey him when he tells them what to do to make Beatrice and Benedick fall in love.
    b) E.g. He persuades Leonato to let Claudio and Hero marry because he wants Claudio to be happy.
2.  E.g. He seems playful as he wants to provide entertainment for himself and others, devising a plan to bring Benedick and Beatrice together so that "time shall not go dully by" until Claudio and Hero's wedding.
3.  E.g. He says "I will join with thee" when Claudio believes Hero has betrayed him. This shows that he feels responsible for Claudio's embarrassment and wants to put things right.
4.  E.g. It suggests he is arrogant because he refuses to accept the possibility that he might be wrong until he sees proof.

## Page 23: Don John

1.  false, true, false, true, false
2.  a) E.g. "You have of late stood out against your brother". (Act 1, Scene 3, lines 19-20)
    b) E.g. "What is he for a fool that betroths himself to unquietness?" (Act 1, Scene 3, lines 45-46)
3.  E.g. Don John might seem unpleasant. He says that he will "bless" himself if he manages to cause trouble for Claudio, which suggests that he will take a lot of satisfaction from seeing another person suffer.
4.  E.g. He resents his lack of power, so he tries to cause trouble for his brother Don Pedro and for others who are more accepted by society than he is, such as Claudio.

# Answers

## Page 24: Leonato

1. b) E.g. He has a playful side and enjoys deception.
   c) E.g. He values the reputation of his family over his own life.
2. a) E.g. "Count, take of me my daughter".
      (Act 2, Scene 1, line 295)
   b) E.g. "I hope to see you one day fitted with a husband".
      (Act 2, Scene 1, lines 55-56)
3. E.g. He wants what is best for Beatrice. He says he will work through many nights to help Beatrice and Benedick to fall in love, which shows his dedication to helping her.
4. E.g. He sees Hero blush and thinks that this is evidence of her guilt. He also thinks it is impossible that respected gentlemen like Claudio and Don Pedro would lie.

## Page 25: Dogberry

1. a) E.g. "Dost thou not suspect my place?" (line 73)
   b) E.g. "Let the Watch come forth." (lines 35-36)
   c) E.g. "Is our whole dissembly appeared?" (line 1)
2. E.g. After Conrade calls him an "ass", Dogberry suggests that he deserves respect because he is "an officer" and "a householder".
3. E.g. Yes, because Dogberry often gets his words mixed up and says the opposite of what he means, which suggests Shakespeare is mocking the poor education of those of low social status. **Or** e.g. No, because Dogberry and the Watch are ultimately responsible for exposing Don John's plot, which none of the noble characters manage to do. This gives a positive impression of people with a low status.
4. E.g. It creates tension for the audience, as they don't know whether Dogberry will manage to inform the appropriate people in time to stop Don John's plot from succeeding.
Task: Here are some points that you might have included:
   • Dogberry's failure to express himself clearly in Act 3, Scene 5 makes Leonato impatient, so he leaves before Dogberry is able to reveal why he has arrested Borachio and Conrade.
   • This means an opportunity to stop Hero from being shamed is lost, as Leonato could have defended Hero at the wedding if he had known about Borachio and Conrade's actions.

## Page 26: Other Characters

1. E.g. She seems crude but intelligent, as she makes witty comments that reveal her rude sense of humour.
2. develop, Ursula, critical, deception, justice
3. E.g. Yes, because the plot to deceive Claudio is Borachio's idea and he plays a key role in the trick, which makes him responsible. **Or** e.g. No, because Don John has a strong desire to hurt Claudio, and without this Borachio wouldn't have suggested his plot at all.
4. E.g. He links the Friar's belief that Hero is innocent to his reputation as a religious figure. The Friar vows that his "reverence", "divinity" and professional calling as a priest can be considered worthless if he is wrong about Hero.

## Page 27: Skills Focus — Making Links

1. Here are some examples you could have used:
   Beatrice — She tells Benedick that she doesn't want a man to "swear" that he loves her. / She asks Benedick "Do not you love me?" in Act 5, Scene 4.
   Benedick — He doesn't understand why Claudio wants to get married because he believes Claudio will have to give up his freedom. / He tells Don Pedro to "get thee a wife!" because he believes marriage will make Don Pedro happy.
2. Here are some examples you could have used:
   Hero — innocent. In Act 3, Scene 4, she suggests that Margaret should be "ashamed" of herself for making a sexual joke. / She blushes when she is accused of being unfaithful to Claudio in Act 4, Scene 1.
   Claudio — suspicious. He suggests that people should "trust no agent" when he believes that Don Pedro has betrayed him. / He immediately interprets Hero's blushing in Act 4, Scene 1 as a sign of her "cunning sin".

Don Pedro — loyal. He keeps his promise to woo Hero on Claudio's behalf in Act 2, Scene 1. / He defends Claudio in Act 5, Scene 1 when Claudio is accused of "villainy".
Don John — villainous. In Act 1, Scene 3, he plots with Borachio and Conrade to destroy Claudio's happiness. / In Act 4, Scene 1, he lies to Leonato when he confirms Don Pedro's claim that Hero is a "common stale".

## Page 28: Practice Questions

Your answers should have an introduction, several paragraphs developing different ideas and a conclusion. You may have covered some of the following points:

1. • Shakespeare uses language to present Beatrice as passionate in this extract. While describing the types of men she would not marry, she begins each description with the phrase "He that". This repetition creates a rhythm in her speech that suggests she is speaking more firmly as the lines go on, which reflects how passionate she feels about what she is saying. An Elizabethan audience might have responded negatively to Beatrice's passionate nature, viewing her as aggressive and disrespectful, as her passion contrasts with the demure behaviour of the ideal Elizabethan woman.
   • Elsewhere in the play, Shakespeare shows that Beatrice is passionate through her relationship with Benedick. In Act 3, Scene 1, she says "Benedick, love on. I will requite thee". By using the imperative form of the verb "love", Shakespeare gives the impression that Beatrice is ordering Benedick to love her, which shows the strength of her feeling when she promises to love him in return. Beatrice's emotional declaration of love for Benedick contrasts with her fierce rejection of love in Act 1, which highlights that her attitude to love has changed but her passionate nature remains.
   • In Act 4, Scene 1, Shakespeare structures the dialogue between Beatrice and Benedick to present Beatrice as passionate. Benedick says "Hear me, Beatrice —", but she cuts him off and proceeds to interrupt him twice more. The fact that she repeatedly speaks over Benedick suggests that she feels so passionately about what she is saying that she cannot stop talking. Beatrice's passion in Act 4, Scene 1 heightens the audience's sympathy for her, as it shows how distressed she is about Hero's rejection at the wedding and how determined she is to seek justice.

2. • In the extract, Shakespeare uses Claudio and Benedick's language to present them as opposites. He juxtaposes Claudio's suggestion that Hero is "a jewel" and "the sweetest lady" he has ever seen with Benedick's belief that she is "too low for a high praise". Claudio's poetic description of Hero as "a jewel" suggests she is precious and desirable, whereas Benedick's words suggest he is unimpressed by her. Their descriptions also reflect their different attitudes to courtly love, a style of courtship practised by some Elizabethan noblemen. A courtly lover would praise and idealise the woman he loved, as Claudio does, while Benedick's criticism of Hero shows that he rejects courtly love.
   • However, both Claudio and Benedick's actions in the play are motivated by honour. Claudio's honour drives him to shame Hero at the altar, and Benedick feels honour-bound to defend Beatrice's cousin by challenging Claudio to a duel. This shows that, although the two men have different loyalties, both are motivated by the desire to defend honour. Claudio seems selfish to the audience, as he acts to protect his own honour, whereas Benedick seems selfless for his desire to protect the honour of Beatrice's family.
   • Shakespeare uses structure to highlight that Claudio and Benedick are both gullible. Act 2, Scene 3 begins with Benedick saying he will never fall in love, and ends with him falling for the trick and admitting he loves Beatrice. Act 3, Scene 2 begins with Claudio making plans for his marriage to Hero, and ends with him falling for Don John's trick and declaring he will "shame her". By mirroring the structure of these two scenes, Shakespeare highlights that both Claudio

# Answers

and Benedick are easily fooled. However, Shakespeare uses the two men's gullible natures for different purposes, as Benedick's creates humour, while Claudio's leads to tragedy.

3. a) • Don Pedro is shown to have the respect of his followers in this extract. His followers repeatedly refer to him using formal titles, such as "your grace" and "my lord". This emphasises how respected he is because, even though he knows Benedick and Claudio well, they still acknowledge his superior social status. The respect shown to Don Pedro by his followers reflects the 16th-century belief in the Great Chain of Being, which claimed that the social order was decided by God. This meant that people of high social status were viewed as being worthy of respect because they had been given their status by God.

• In the extract, Don Pedro is shown to fulfil a caring, father-like role in his relationship with Claudio and Benedick. He notices that Beatrice has put Benedick "down" and asks Claudio why he is "sad". This shows that Don Pedro is aware of the emotional wellbeing of his followers and considers it his responsibility to ensure their happiness. Having observed in this scene how much Don Pedro cares about his followers, the audience might forgive him more easily for his part in shaming Hero later in the play, as they might recognise that he is acting out of concern for Claudio.

• Don Pedro is presented as loyal to the men who follow him. When Claudio believes Don Pedro has betrayed him, Don Pedro assures Beatrice that Claudio is mistaken, saying "I'll be sworn" that Claudio has no reason to be jealous. The word "sworn" is associated with making an oath, which is a solemn promise that you swear not to break. This highlights that Don Pedro has kept his word to Claudio and is a loyal friend to him. Shakespeare contrasts Don Pedro's loyalty in the extract with Claudio's mistrust, which shows that Don Pedro's loyalty to his followers is not always returned.

b) • Observations play a key role in the tricks that lead to the development of Benedick and Beatrice's relationship. In Act 2, Scene 3, Don Pedro says "See you where Benedick hath hid himself?" when Benedick hides in the "arbour". This observation highlights that Don Pedro and the rest know that Benedick is hiding nearby and will overhear their conversation. This is crucial to the success of the trick, as they need Benedick to overhear and believe their claims that Beatrice loves him. Shakespeare reinforces the importance of observations in the trick by making puns about 'noting' (observing) before the deception begins, when Balthasar says "Note this before my notes."

• False observations are important for the development of the plot. Claudio humiliates Hero at the altar after he and Don Pedro are "witnesses" to her infidelity. The word 'witness' is often associated with observing a crime, emphasising Claudio's belief that he has observed Hero being unfaithful, and this is what motivates him to shame her at the wedding. The fact that Claudio's false observation is believed over Hero's denial highlights that the men in the play have more control over events in the plot than the women do. This reflects the greater social influence of 16th-century men compared to women.

• Shakespeare's comedies often involve young lovers, and Claudio's observation of Hero early in the play signals to the audience that this play will follow that convention. In Act 1, Scene 1, Claudio asks Benedick, "didst thou note the daughter of Signior Leonato?" and calls Hero a "modest young lady". This suggests that Claudio has been observing Hero and has judged her to be a woman he would like to marry. The play continues to follow the conventions of a comedy by having the young lovers face a problem that they must overcome when Hero is accused of being unfaithful as a result of a false observation.

4. • In the extract, Leonato's discussion of emotion highlights his maturity. He says the "load of sorrow" is harder to "endure" personally than it seems when other people experience it.

Leonato's ability to take a critical view of his emotions and question how and why they affect different people emphasises his maturity to the audience. Describing grief as a "load" metaphorically likens it to a heavy weight, emphasising how difficult and painful it is to experience grief. Leonato's ability to bear this level of grief with grace and dignity further highlights his maturity.

• Elsewhere in the play, Leonato is presented as mature through his response to Claudio's treatment of Hero. In Act 5, Scene 1, Leonato says that his desire for "revenge" will die if Claudio agrees to marry Hero's 'cousin', despite the insult Claudio has done to their family. In the 16th century, women were expected to marry so that their husbands could provide for them, and Leonato's focus on achieving this for Hero shows his maturity and his ability to look at the bigger picture. A modern audience, lacking 16th-century expectations about marriage, might view Leonato's attitude as cold rather than mature, feeling he should reject Claudio for his harsh treatment of Hero.

• Leonato is shown to be mature through his role as the head of his household. In Act 2, Scene 1, he says he is willing to sacrifice "ten nights'" sleep to help get Beatrice a good husband. This shows how hard he is willing to work to help Beatrice, which shows that he cares about the people in his household and feels a sense of responsibility towards them. Shakespeare highlights Leonato's role as the head of his household from the play's opening lines, as he is the recipient of the messenger's letter, which immediately shows the audience that he is a mature and authoritative character.

## Section Three — Context and Themes

### Page 29: Honour and Reputation

1. male, admirable, battle, foolishly, Hero
2. E.g. Claudio has dishonoured Leonato's daughter and Leonato wants to restore his family's honour in a duel.
3. a) E.g. Don Pedro is angry that he and Claudio have been dishonoured by their association with a supposedly unfaithful woman, so he shames Hero with Claudio.
   b) E.g. Don Pedro and Claudio are seen as honourable men, which means their accusations are powerful. Without her good reputation, Hero is viewed as "rotten" and her claims of innocence are seen as worthless.

### Pages 30-31: Love and Marriage

1. true, true, false, false
2. E.g. In Act 2, Scene 1, when Claudio is told that he can marry Hero, Leonato says "take of me my daughter", but Hero says nothing. This reflects that Leonato's decision is the only one that matters.
3. a) E.g. This suggests Claudio wants to marry a rich woman, as he is interested in what Hero will inherit from Leonato.
   b) E.g. This suggests that Claudio is happy to marry someone he doesn't know in order to earn Leonato's forgiveness.
4. E.g. Benedick and Beatrice enjoy bickering with each other and have lots of interactions during the play, but Claudio and Hero barely speak to each other.
5. woo, follows, ignores, superficial, know
6. E.g. Love seems grand and important. Shakespeare writes in verse, which makes love seem noble and impressive, and uses poetic language such as "soft and delicate desires", which suggests love can't be described in simple terms.
7. E.g. It suggests that there are different ways to be in love. Benedick and Beatrice can't "woo peaceably", but they enjoy teasing each other and are happy together.
8. E.g. They suggest that Benedick and Beatrice are struggling with their changing feelings about love, and that this affects them so deeply that it is comparable to being unwell.

# Answers

Task: You should have written your letter from Claudio's point of
view. You may have included some of the following points:
- Claudio is a count. This gives him a high social status, which
means he can give Hero the sort of life she is used to as a
noblewoman.
- Claudio has gained honour in battle. This means he is
well-respected by others, which suggests he will make a
suitable husband for Hero.
- Claudio has traditional values. He takes a conventional
approach to love and marriage, which suggests he is a
respectable gentleman.

## Pages 32-33: Deception and Misunderstanding

1. b) E.g. He suggests the plan to shame Hero in return for money. /
He is willing to use deception for his own benefit.
   c) E.g. She tricks Beatrice into believing Benedick is in love with
her. / She is happy to deceive others if it is to help someone she
cares about.
2. a) E.g. Dogberry misunderstands the crime that has been
committed and accuses Borachio of theft.
   b) E.g. It highlights Dogberry's incompetence as he can't recognise
a crime when the proof is right in front of him.
3. E.g. The fishing imagery makes the deception seem like a trap
that will capture Benedick. / The fishing imagery makes the
deception seem like an enjoyable sport for the men.
4. E.g. These deceptions are done with good intentions, as their
friends think Benedick and Beatrice would be well-matched
and are helping to bring them together.
5. a) E.g. "he is the Prince's jester, a very dull fool". (line 133)
   b) E.g. "I know you well enough. You are Signior Antonio."
(line 109)
6. You should have ticked the second and fourth statements.
7. E.g. Friar Francis notes Hero and understands correctly, which
shows his wisdom in contrast to the other characters.
8. E.g. It suggests that appearances can be deceiving because
something that looks "fair" might be "foul" in reality.
9. E.g. To highlight how widespread deception is in the play.
So much deception has taken place that the only way to
resolve everything is with yet more trickery.

Exam Practice:
Your answer should have an introduction, several paragraphs
developing different ideas and a conclusion. You may have
covered some of the following points:
- In this extract, Shakespeare shows that misunderstandings
can make people look foolish. Antonio claims in the extract
that "The Prince" (Don Pedro) wants to marry Hero. By
placing this scene directly after Claudio's confession of his
love for Hero in Act 1, Scene 1, Shakespeare ensures that
the audience already knows Antonio's claims are false,
which makes Antonio look foolish. Antonio's foolishness
in this scene contrasts with the expectations an Elizabethan
audience might have had of him, as older men of high social
status would normally be viewed as wise and respectable.
- Elsewhere in the play, misunderstandings are shown to
be damaging. In Act 4, Scene 1, Hero "blushes" as she
is accused. Blushing is a sign of her innocence, but
Claudio misunderstands and takes it as proof of her guilt,
confirming his suspicions that she has been unfaithful and is
covering her "cunning sin". This reinforces how damaging
misunderstandings can be. The word "sin" implies that
Hero's actions are an insult to God as well as to Claudio,
which highlights how seriously Hero is criticised as a result
of Claudio's misunderstanding.
- As the play is a comedy, many of the misunderstandings
are presented as humorous. For example, Dogberry
often misunderstands what people say to him, such as
when Leonato calls him "tedious" and Dogberry takes it
as a compliment. Dogberry's lack of awareness of what
Leonato really means creates humour for the audience,
because it shows his ignorance. Clown characters are a
common feature of Shakespeare's comedies, so Dogberry's

misunderstandings would have helped an Elizabethan
audience identify him as this type of character.

## Pages 34-35: Gender

1. E.g. He says that she must accept Don Pedro if he proposes to
her. / He agrees that Claudio can marry her in Act 2, Scene 1.
/ He agrees that she will pretend to be dead. / He decides that
Claudio can marry her in Act 5, Scene 4.
2. a) E.g. They might have been surprised that a woman would reject
an advantageous marriage to a high-status prince.
   b) E.g. They might have thought it was the right thing to do
because unmarried women often couldn't live independently.
3. a) E.g. Hero is a "maid" before she gets married. / Margaret makes
sexual jokes in Act 5, Scene 2.
   b) E.g. Hero doesn't question Leonato's commands in Act 2,
Scene 1. / Beatrice is outspoken and critical of Benedick in
Act 2, Scene 1.
4. E.g. Don Pedro and Claudio mock Benedick for his desire not
to get married, which suggests they see it as strange.
5. E.g. It suggests that they think women are likely to be unfaithful
to their husbands. This shows that they view women as disloyal
and untrustworthy.
6. a) E.g. Hero is mostly silent. / Hero speaks confidently and
criticises Beatrice.
   b) E.g. There are no men around in Act 3, Scene 1 so she feels
able to ignore the expectation that women should be quiet.
7. E.g. If she was a man, she would be able to get justice for Hero,
but as a woman she is unable to challenge Claudio.
8. E.g. Yes, because she loves Benedick. She and Benedick are
both unconventional and can have a relationship on their own
terms, ignoring society's expectations surrounding love and
marriage. **Or** e.g. No, because she has changed who she is
in order to conform to society's expectations. She will have
to give up her independence by marrying, which is reflected
when Benedick says "I will stop your mouth."

## Page 36: Loyalty

1. a) E.g. This emphasises Beatrice's desire to defend Hero and try to
get revenge for her when she is shamed by Claudio.
   b) E.g. Don Pedro shows loyalty to Claudio by supporting him
when Claudio believes he has been wronged by Hero.
2. E.g. Don Pedro and Don John are brothers, and family loyalty
was important in the 16th century. / He trusted that Don John
wouldn't betray his family a second time.
3. E.g. It suggests that Beatrice values loyalty highly, as she is
criticising Benedick by saying he is changeable and disloyal in
his friendships.
4. a) E.g. Don Pedro tells Claudio "I have wooed in thy name",
which shows he has kept his promise from Act 1, Scene 1.
   b) E.g. They might view him as foolish and suspicious, as
Don Pedro has given Claudio no reason to doubt his loyalty.

## Page 37: Skills Focus — Writing about Context

1. a) Shakespeare uses his presentation of the Watch in the play
to mock the real Elizabethan Watch, who were generally
considered to be useless.
   b) This plays on Claudio's fear of being cuckolded, which was a
serious concern for men in Shakespeare's time. / which reflects
the belief held by many men in the 16th century that women
were untrustworthy.
2. Piece of context: 2
Explanation of choice: The P.E.E.D. explanation bullet states
that Beatrice is unique among the female characters because
she challenges male characters. The second piece of context
explains why this would have been significant to Shakespeare's
audience.

# Answers

## Page 38: Practice Questions

Your answers should have an introduction, several paragraphs developing different ideas and a conclusion. You may have covered some of the following points:

1. • In this extract, Shakespeare uses Claudio to suggest that loyalties can easily change. When Claudio is told that Hero has been unfaithful to him, he says he will "shame" her. This harsh reaction highlights that Claudio's instinct is to be suspicious of Hero and to punish her, rather than to be loyal and trust she has been faithful. Claudio's line "where I should wed, there will I shame her" emphasises his changing loyalty. The contrast between the verbs "should", which refers to past intentions, and "will", which implies future intentions, suggests his love for Hero is in the past and now he is focused on revenge.

   • Shakespeare structures the play to emphasise his criticism of Claudio's disloyalty. In Act 1, Scene 1, Leonato says that Don Pedro has "bestowed much honour" upon Claudio, but in Act 2, Scene 1, Claudio easily believes Don Pedro has betrayed him. By presenting Don Pedro as a loyal friend from the start of the play, Shakespeare makes Claudio's later mistrust seem unfounded. This shows Claudio to be disloyal for believing Don John's lies about his friend. Loyalty was an important aspect of the code of honour followed by many Elizabethan noblemen, so Claudio's disloyalty may have caused Shakespeare's audience to respond negatively to his character.

   • Elsewhere in the play, Shakespeare suggests that Claudio's disloyalty to Hero has serious consequences for him. Beatrice asks Benedick to "Kill Claudio" after Claudio mistreats Hero, prompting Benedick to challenge Claudio to a duel in Act 5, Scene 1. This shows that Benedick and Beatrice want to hold Claudio to account for his disloyalty to Hero and refuse to let his behaviour go unpunished. The audience is encouraged to respond positively to Benedick's choice to challenge Claudio, suggesting that it is a fitting response to Claudio's disloyalty and that Claudio deserves to be punished for it.

2. a) • Shakespeare suggests that innocence is more difficult to believe than guilt. When Beatrice says she did not sleep in Hero's room the night before the wedding, Leonato believes the accusation against Hero is "Confirmed, confirmed!" The repetition of "confirmed" makes Leonato sound adamant, showing that he strongly believes in Hero's guilt and is ignoring her claims of innocence. The men's readiness to believe that Hero is unfaithful reflects that many men in the 16th century felt women could not be trusted and were likely to betray their husbands.

   • The language in this extract links innocence with purity and goodness. Friar Francis says the "angel whiteness" of Hero's face supports her claims of innocence. The colour white is associated with purity, while the religious imagery created by "angel" gives an impression of virtue and holiness, emphasising that Hero is innocent. The association of innocence with piety is reinforced in by the fact that it is Friar Francis, a moral and respected religious figure, who draws the link between them.

   • Shakespeare suggests that innocence can be a source of strength. Hero tells Leonato to "Refuse me, hate me, torture me to death!" if she is guilty. Hero's willingness to put herself forward for extreme punishments such as "torture" highlights her certainty that her innocence will be proven and that she will not have to suffer the punishments she describes. These assertive lines from Hero contrast with her quiet and demure manner elsewhere in the play, which reinforces the strength that certainty of her innocence has given her.

   b) • The characters in the play are very aware of everyone's social status. In Act 2, Scene 1, Beatrice rejects Don Pedro's proposal of marriage because he is "too costly to wear every day". This clothing metaphor suggests that Don Pedro's social status is as visible as the clothes he is wearing and can be gauged just by looking at him, while "costly" suggests that Beatrice is aware of the responsibilities that come with having a high status and rejects them because they would come at an expense to her. This highlights to the audience that being high-born can be a burden in a society where everyone takes notice of the social status of others.

   • Social status is an important aspect of Don Pedro's relationships with other characters. For example, he controls the plan to trick Benedick and Beatrice into falling in love by giving orders to lower-status characters. These orders are obeyed without question, which suggests that Don Pedro, the character in the play with the highest social status, is seen as a figure of authority who should be obeyed. The deference shown to Don Pedro by lower-status characters reflects the 16th-century belief that the social order was decided by God and that it was therefore important to maintain a strict social hierarchy.

   • As in many of his other comedies, Shakespeare includes low-status characters in *Much Ado About Nothing* to create humour. Dogberry is a "poor man" who uses lots of malapropisms in his speech, such as saying "odorous" when he means 'odious'. Dogberry's mistakes with language provide a comic contrast to the main plot involving the noble characters, which contains elements of tragedy as well as comedy. However, in addition to this, low-status characters are also portrayed positively. For example, Dogberry is well-meaning and honest, in contrast to many of the noble characters.

3. • In this extract, Hero defies the expectations of female behaviour that an Elizabethan audience would have held by being confident and playful. She criticises Beatrice, saying "Disdain and scorn ride sparkling in her eyes". The word "sparkling", which creates an impression of brightness and energy, makes Hero's language seem dramatic, suggesting that she is painting a vivid picture of Beatrice with her words. This use of language reflects Hero's confidence and her enjoyment of the trick, which does not conform to 16th-century expectations that women should be quiet and gentle. Hero's sharp words in this extract show a different side to her character, contrasting with her demure behaviour earlier in the play.

   • Throughout the play, Beatrice's behaviour might be seen as unconventional by an Elizabethan audience. In Act 2, Scene 1, she is outspoken about her disinterest in marriage, saying that she views having no husband as a "blessing". This attitude to marriage defies the Elizabethans' belief that a woman's purpose was to become a wife and mother. When Shakespeare was writing Beatrice, he might have been influenced by the behaviour of Elizabeth I, who ruled England when he was writing and who defied expectations by refusing to marry.

   • However, women are often presented as subservient to men in the play, which is particularly shown through the character of Hero. In Act 2, Scene 1, Hero is silent as Leonato tells her "you know your answer" when she receives a marriage proposal. This shows that, like many 16th-century women, Hero is not allowed to make her own decisions and is controlled by the men in her life. A modern audience might respond negatively to Hero's subservient behaviour, wishing that she would question the men or stand up for herself, as 21st-century women are expected to be more confident and independent.

4. • In this extract, Shakespeare uses Borachio to highlight that honour needs to be defended. Borachio knows that Don John can manipulate Don Pedro and Claudio by claiming that their "honour" and "reputation" will be damaged by their association with a "contaminated stale". This suggests that Borachio is certain Don Pedro and Claudio will do whatever is necessary to protect their reputations from potential damage. Borachio's use of the word

# Answers

"contaminated", which is associated with disease, suggests that Hero's dishonour could infect Claudio and Don Pedro too. This further emphasises the need for them to defend their honour.
- Elsewhere in the play, Shakespeare suggests that honour is worth dying for. In Act 5, Scene 1, Leonato tries to get justice for Hero's poor treatment by challenging Claudio to a duel, even though he is an old man with "grey hairs and bruise of many days". This shows that Leonato is willing to risk his life to defend his family's honour. Leonato's determination to protect his family's reputation, regardless of the consequences for himself, might make an audience view him more favourably and forgive his anger towards Hero in Act 4, Scene 1.
- Shakespeare uses Hero to show that women are viewed as worthless without their honour. After Hero is accused of being unfaithful, Leonato says "Let her die." This extreme reaction highlights Leonato's belief that his daughter would be better off dead than living with a damaged reputation, which emphasises how serious the loss of Hero's honour is. Hero's situation reflects that, in Shakespeare's time, noblewomen were valued primarily as wives and mothers. Without a good reputation, a 16th-century woman would be less likely to make a good marriage, and would therefore be seen as worthless.

## Section Four — Shakespeare's Techniques

### Pages 39-40: Form and Structure

1. Disguises: e.g. Hero wears a mask when she pretends to be her 'cousin'.
   Music: e.g. Balthasar sings a hymn at Hero's tomb.
   Puns and wordplay: e.g. "Mark how short his answer is — with Hero, Leonato's short daughter." (lines 200-201)
2. false, true, false
3. a) E.g. Dogberry tries to interrogate the prisoners but keeps saying the wrong words, which is amusing for the audience.
   b) E.g. To lighten the mood of the play, as this scene comes immediately after the tragic scene when Hero is shamed.
4. E.g. The tragic elements make the audience more invested in the play. For example, Hero's unfair treatment makes the audience hope that her innocence will be proved.
5. relationships, Hero, tension, climax, rejects
6. E.g. To reinforce the sense of threat from the previous scene when Don John said he wanted to hurt Claudio. The fact he is "melancholy" reminds the audience he wants revenge.
7. E.g. The ending of Act 2, Scene 1 mirrors the ending of Act 1, Scene 1. Both scenes end with Don Pedro explaining his plan to bring a couple together.
8. E.g. It suggests the play is speeding towards a resolution, creating a sense of building excitement for the audience.
9. E.g. To create a light-hearted mood on stage and reinforce the happy ending for the audience.

### Page 41: Dramatic Irony

1. a) E.g. The audience knows that Don John has lied to Claudio about Don Pedro's motives. / It is frustrating for the audience that Claudio believes Don John's lies so easily.
   b) E.g. The audience knows that Dogberry isn't "wise" because they have seen how incompetent he is at his job. / It is humorous for the audience because it highlights Dogberry's false pride.
2. a) E.g. He thinks that the claims that Beatrice loves him were "no trick", but the audience knows they were exactly that.
   b) E.g. The audience knows that Beatrice is behaving as she normally does, so it is funny that Benedick interprets her behaviour differently and is now convinced she loves him.
3. E.g. It creates tension for the audience as they have to wait to find out if and how her innocence will be proved.

### Page 42: Mood and Atmosphere

1. E.g. It creates a threatening mood, because it reveals how determined Don John is to get revenge.
2. a) E.g. A relaxed atmosphere. The references to "honeysuckles" and the shady "pleached bower" suggest tranquil surroundings.
   b) E.g. A sombre atmosphere. The stage is lit by "tapers", suggesting it is dimly lit, which creates a serious mood.
3. E.g. The song introduces a sense of uncertainty by suggesting that men are "deceivers" who commit "fraud".
4. a) E.g. A hostile mood. The idea of eating a "heart" is violent and gruesome, which creates a sense of threat.
   b) E.g. A chilling mood. The word "poison" encourages the audience to think of death, which creates a sense of horror.
Task: You should have written your answer in the style of a diary entry. Here are some points you may have included:
- The atmosphere is tense at the start of the scene before Hero is accused. It is clear that something isn't right, as Claudio sharply answers "No" when asked if he'll marry Hero, suggesting the wedding won't happen as expected.
- There is a threatening atmosphere when Claudio accuses Hero. His harsh language, such as when he calls Hero an "approved wanton", shows how angry he is.
- The atmosphere becomes more tragic as Hero tries and fails to persuade the men she is innocent. Her exclamations, such as "How am I beset!", emphasise how distressed and helpless she is.

### Pages 43-44: Poetry and Prose

1. false, true, false, true, false
2. a) E.g. "Prince, thou art sad. Get thee a wife, get thee a wife!" (lines 120-121)
   b) E.g. "Meantime let wonder seem familiar, / And to the chapel let us presently." (lines 70-71)
   c) E.g. "And got a calf in that same noble feat / Much like to you, for you have just his bleat." (lines 50-51)
3. E.g. To make the dialogue sound informal, which suggests that the men are good friends and reflects the casual, witty nature of their conversation.
4. E.g. To make the language sound more formal, which reflects the solemn nature of Claudio's mourning. This highlights his grief and heightens the tragedy of the scene for the audience.
5. E.g. To make the lines seem more dramatic, which shows the strength of Leonato's anger and his desire for revenge as he challenges Claudio to a duel.
6. E.g. Prose makes their speech sound natural, suggesting that Benedick and Beatrice are comfortable in each other's company. This makes their love seem honest and genuine.
7. E.g. The rhythm of the blank verse places emphasis on certain words, such as "fair", which highlights Claudio's praise of Hero and emphasises his romantic feelings for her. / Claudio's use of blank verse associates him with traditional courtly lovers, who often wrote poetry and used poetic language to woo their desired partner.
8. a) E.g. It shows he has a vulnerable side, as he feels hurt by Beatrice's insults, such as her suggestion that he is a "fool".
   b) E.g. The soliloquy is quite short, which suggests Benedick doesn't want to reflect on his feelings for too long.
Task: You may have included some of the following points:
- In Act 1, Scene 1, the men use prose to discuss Benedick's dislike of marriage but use blank verse to talk about Claudio's love for Hero. This highlights the contrast between Benedick and Claudio's attitudes to love.
- In Act 4, Scene 1, the scene starts in prose but switches to blank verse when Claudio starts accusing Hero. Verse is associated with being noble and honourable, so this reflects Claudio's belief that he is right to shame Hero.

### Page 45: Imagery and Symbolism

1. "She's limed, I warrant you: we have caught her, madam." (line 104) / "Some Cupid kills with arrows, some with traps." (line 106)

# Answers

2.  E.g. War is associated with violence and hostility, which reflects the argumentative nature of their relationship.
3.  a) Metaphor / E.g. It exaggerates the difficulty of Don Pedro's task by comparing it to the 'impossible' labours of Hercules.
    b) Simile / E.g. It highlights the pain that Benedick's unrequited love causes him by describing him as a dying fire.
    c) Personification / E.g. It makes the audience view revenge as a living thing that can influence others, emphasising how powerful it is.
4.  E.g. It symbolises Benedick's attitude to friendship by suggesting that he changes his loyalties as quickly and as easily as he changes his "hat".

## Page 46: Puns and Wordplay

1.  meaning, pronounced, funny, humour
2.  E.g. Both meanings of "canker" emphasise that Don John is an unpleasant character and that he has no desire to change his behaviour or try to make people like him.
3.  E.g. The jokes are an important source of comedy in the play, as they make the audience laugh by demonstrating the characters' skill with witty wordplay. / They show the male characters' lack of trust in women by highlighting the belief held by many men in the 16th century that women were likely to be unfaithful to their husbands.
4.  E.g. Dogberry is talking about Borachio and Conrade, who are criminals, so it is humorous that he is unintentionally praising them rather than criticising them.

## Page 47: Other Language Techniques

1.  a) E.g. He contrasts the opposing ideas of life and death.
    b) E.g. The reference to life suggests that there is still hope for a happy ending, despite the tragedy of Hero's 'death'.
2.  E.g. Don Pedro is presented as warm and gracious, saying "my dear friend Leonato", which shows his affection for his host. Don John only has one short line, which makes him seem less open and friendly than Don Pedro.
3.  E.g. It shows the plan will hurt lots of people, making it sound more villainous.
4.  a) E.g. It emphasises Beatrice's clever use of wordplay that transforms Benedick's words into something disgusting.
    b) E.g. It emphasises Don Pedro's shock at seeing Hero alive when he believed that she was dead.

Exam Practice:
Your answer should have an introduction, several paragraphs developing different ideas and a conclusion. You may have covered some of the following points:
- In this extract, Shakespeare uses Benedick to highlight that betrayal is seen as something that can be easily forgiven. Benedick says that he had expected to fight Claudio but now hopes Claudio will "live unbruised". This shows that Benedick is no longer angry with Claudio for his betrayal of Hero, as he was in Act 5, Scene 1 when he challenged Claudio to a duel. Benedick's willingness to forgive is a result of the play's form, as a happy ending is an important feature of Shakespeare's comedies, which means any problems must be resolved by the final scene.
- Shakespeare uses language to highlight that the men in the play are afraid of being betrayed by women. In Act 1, Scene 1, Benedick says he should have "bull's horns" stuck into his forehead if he ever gets married. This cuckold imagery reflects the worries of men in Shakespeare's time about being betrayed by women, as Elizabethans joked that men with unfaithful wives would grow horns. Shakespeare also structures the play to emphasise the men's distrust. He uses cuckold jokes at the start and end of the play, which shows that the men's fear of betrayal does not change.
- Shakespeare uses Claudio to explore the anger that people can feel when they are betrayed. In Act 2, Scene 1, Claudio says to "trust no agent" after he thinks Don Pedro has betrayed him. This pessimistic statement makes him sound bitter and resentful, showing how angry he feels about

supposedly being betrayed by Don Pedro. The strength of Claudio's anger is further emphasised by using the imperative form of the verb "trust", which makes his words sound like a command, highlighting the firmness of his belief and his determination not to make the same mistake again.

## Page 48: Skills Focus — Working with Extracts

1.  E.g. Before the extract, Claudio accused Hero of being unfaithful. Leonato is about to say he believes Claudio.
2.  E.g. "For thee I'll lock up all the gates of love"
3.  E.g. It emphasises Claudio's belief that Hero's true nature is the opposite of what her outward appearance suggests.
4.  E.g. In Act 2, Scene 1, Claudio believes Don John when he tells him that Don Pedro is in love with Hero.

## Page 49: Practice Questions

Your answers should have an introduction, several paragraphs developing different ideas and a conclusion. You may have covered some of the following points:
1.  a) • Shakespeare uses the setting in this extract to create a sombre atmosphere. The scene takes place at "the monument of Leonato", which is Leonato's family tomb. Tombs are associated with death and mourning, which immediately suggests to the audience that this will be a solemn scene. Shakespeare reinforces the sombre atmosphere that is created by this setting by using chilling imagery of death in Claudio's speech about Hero, such as "unto thy bones good night!"
    • Shakespeare highlights Claudio's grief to create a sombre atmosphere. Claudio says he will come "Yearly" to Hero's tomb and mourn for her. This suggests that his sorrow for Hero's death and his guilt over the part he played in it will stay with him forever, which heightens the feeling of sadness for the audience. Balthasar's song further heightens the sombre atmosphere by reinforcing Claudio's grief, as the repetition of "Heavily, heavily" suggests that Claudio's grief is so strong that it is physically weighing him down.
    • Shakespeare uses song lyrics to increase the sombre atmosphere in this scene. Balthasar sings a "solemn hymn" for Hero, which contains lots of words associated with despair, such as "woe" and "groan". The language in this song helps to create a mournful atmosphere, which reinforces the sombre nature of this scene. Shakespeare also uses song lyrics to influence the play's atmosphere in Act 2, Scene 3, when Balthasar refers to the "woe" that is caused by the "fraud of men", which foreshadows the tragic events still to come in the play.
    b) • Shakespeare uses structure to highlight the close relationship between Beatrice and Hero. When Beatrice asks about "Signior Mountanto" in Act 1, Scene 1, Hero knows "My cousin means Signior Benedick". Shakespeare places Hero's explanation after both the Messenger and Leonato have spoken and failed to understand Beatrice's meaning, which emphasises that Hero knows Beatrice better than they do. The fact that Hero's only line in Act 1, Scene 1 is about Beatrice highlights Beatrice's importance to her, further reinforcing that they have a close relationship.
    • Shakespeare shows that Beatrice is protective of Hero. In Act 4, Scene 1, Shakespeare highlights Beatrice's outrage at Hero's unfair treatment when she says that Claudio "slandered, scorned, dishonoured my kinswoman". This list of three verbs in a row suggests Beatrice's anger is growing as she speaks, while the word "kinswoman" highlights the sense of responsibility she feels towards Hero because of their family connection. Shakespeare also emphasises the strength of Beatrice's protective feelings through her request for Benedick to "Kill Claudio", as this shows that Beatrice is willing to go to extremes to protect Hero.
    • Shakespeare shows that Hero cares about Beatrice. In Act 2, Scene 1, she agrees to Don Pedro's plan in order to help Beatrice "to a good husband". This shows that she thinks Beatrice and Benedick would be a well-matched couple

# Answers

and believes it is in Beatrice's best interests for them to get married. Hero's concern for Beatrice conforms to the stereotype of the ideal Elizabethan woman, as women were expected to be caring and nurturing, traits associated with their primary role in society as wives and mothers.

2. • As in many of his comedies, Shakespeare presents love as a key feature of the play's happy ending. In this extract, Benedick "Kisses" Beatrice and says he will marry her. This confirmation of their romantic relationship concludes their plotline and signals that the characters have been given a happy ending, which is consistent with the comedic form of the play. Unlike an Elizabethan audience, a modern audience might react negatively to this ending, as they might not see it as admirable that Beatrice gives up her rebellion against expectation in order to marry Benedick.
   • Elsewhere in the play, Shakespeare shows that love can be fragile. In Act 1, Scene 1, Claudio is desperate for Hero to be his "wife", but after Don John tricks him in Act 2, Scene 1, he says "Farewell" to the idea of marrying her. Claudio falls in love rapidly then disregards his love for Hero just as quickly based on a single lie, suggesting that his feelings are not strong enough to overcome obstacles in the relationship. This reinforces Shakespeare's message that relationships based on courtly love can be superficial, suggesting that this traditional approach to love followed by many Elizabethan noblemen is flawed.
   • In the play, Shakespeare presents love as something that can change people. In Act 2, Scene 3, Benedick says that Claudio used to "speak plain" but now his words are "a very fantastical banquet". The metaphor of a "fantastical banquet" creates an impression of extravagance and excess, which suggests that Claudio's speech has become like the poetic style of a traditional courtly lover. The contrast between this and Claudio's old life as a "plain" soldier emphasises that he has become a different person since falling in love. The drastic nature of this change emphasises to the audience that love is a powerful force.

3. • Shakespeare uses language to suggest that deception can be enjoyable. In this extract, Claudio says "Stalk on, stalk on" when Don Pedro begins tricking Benedick. The repetition of "Stalk on" makes Claudio sound eager, as though he is encouraging Don Pedro and is excited about the outcome, which gives the impression that he finds deception entertaining. The audience might view Claudio and Don Pedro negatively for deceiving Benedick for their enjoyment, but they might also feel that they are acting in Benedick's best interests by helping him to get married.
   • Deception is presented as widespread. Throughout the play, Don John and his follower Borachio conspire to deceive others, while in Act 3, Scene 1, Hero works with her servants to deceive Beatrice. The fact that deception features at all levels of the 16th-century social hierarchy, from servants to princes, would have emphasised the widespread nature of deception for Shakespeare's audience. Shakespeare also uses structure to emphasise this, as three consecutive scenes from Act 2, Scene 3 to Act 3, Scene 2 all involve a main character being deceived, making the deception seem relentless.
   • Shakespeare shows that deception can have serious consequences. In Act 4, Scene 1, Hero is rejected by Claudio and threatened with being sent to a nunnery. This shows that Don John's deception would have ruined Hero's life if the truth had not been discovered. However, the fact that the play is a comedy prevents the audience from seeing the deception as too harmful. They know the play will end happily, which means the deceptions will not cause any lasting trouble.

4. • In this extract, Benedick is presented as honourable when he challenges Claudio to a duel. He accuses Claudio of having "killed a sweet lady". Benedick's description of Hero as "sweet" highlights his recognition that she is innocent. His desire to defend an innocent woman against unjust treatment

makes him seem honourable. His actions might have seemed particularly honourable to an Elizabethan audience, as in Shakespeare's time duels were often used to solve disputes over honour, and Benedick's actions suggest that he is willing to die to protect the honour of others.
   • Elsewhere in the play, Shakespeare presents Benedick as suspicious of women. In Act 1, Scene 1, Benedick uses cuckold imagery to describe his dislike of marriage, saying married men wear caps "with suspicion" to hide horns underneath. This reference to cuckolds highlights Benedick's belief that women are likely to be unfaithful to their husbands so should not be trusted. A modern audience might react negatively to this attitude, as it shows Benedick is prejudiced against women, whereas an Elizabethan audience might have found it humorous, because this attitude was accepted in Shakespeare's time.
   • Benedick is presented as a confident character. In Act 1, Scene 1, he says that he will "die" for his opinion about love "at the stake". In the 16th century, those with views that went against accepted religious beliefs could be executed by being burnt at the stake. Benedick's choice of language suggests that he is aware that his view is unpopular in society, but is determined to hold it and openly express it anyway. This shows his confidence in himself. Elsewhere in the play, Benedick shows vulnerability, such as when he is hurt by Beatrice's insults in Act 2, Scene 1. This makes his confidence seem less assured and prevents him from seeming too arrogant to the audience.

## Section Five — Exam Buster

### Page 50: Understanding the Question

1. b) Write about the significance of Don John in the play.
   c) Explain how the relationship between Claudio and Hero is presented.
   d) Write about the importance of disloyalty in *Much Ado About Nothing*.
   e) How does Shakespeare use Hero to explore the theme of reputation?
   f) How is the theme of gender presented in *Much Ado About Nothing*?
   g) Explain how Shakespeare presents Leonato in *Much Ado About Nothing*.

2. a - 2, b - 4, c - 1, d - 3, e - 5

### Page 51: Making a Rough Plan

1. E.g. Shakespeare uses Benedick's attitude to suggest that marriage can be painful. / Marriage is presented as necessary. / Shakespeare shows that marriage is a cause for celebration.
2. Pick your three most important points and put them in a sensible order. Write down a quote or example from the text to back up each one.

### Page 52: Making Links

1. E.g. Don Pedro says his brother is "composed and framed of treachery" in Act 5, Scene 1.
   E.g. He spreads lies about Don Pedro, telling Claudio that he woos Hero for himself.
   E.g. Other characters believe his lies because he is an influential prince.
2. E.g. If one of your points was 'Marriage is presented as necessary', and your evidence was that Benedick says "the world must be peopled", another example could be that in Act 2, Scene 1, Leonato tells Hero that she must accept a marriage proposal from Don Pedro.

### Page 53: Structuring Your Answer

1. Point: Shakespeare uses Leonato to highlight the importance of a good reputation.
   Example: In Act 4, Scene 1, Leonato says "Death is the fairest cover" for Hero's "shame".

# Answers

Explanation: This shows that Leonato believes it is better for his own child to be dead than to live in dishonour, which suggests that he views Hero's loss of reputation as an extremely serious setback that cannot be reversed.

Develop: Leonato's attitude reflects the 16th-century belief that honour and a good reputation were worth dying for.

2. a) E.g. Leonato says Beatrice has "an enraged affection" for Benedick.

   b) E.g. Claudio suggests Hero has a "blot" on her reputation.

3. Point: Shakespeare uses Benedick's attitude to suggest that marriage can be painful.

   Example: Benedick says that he would rather be hung "in a bottle" while people "shoot" at him than fall in love and get married.

   Explanation: This exaggeration emphasises how opposed Benedick is to the idea of marriage by linking it to being attacked and injured.

   Develop: This highlights the power of love when Benedick changes his mind later in the play, as he shows his willingness to expose himself to the 'pain' he mocked before.

## Page 54: Introductions and Conclusions

1. Intro b) is better, e.g. Intro b) sets out the points for the answer to build on, while a) makes a point and starts analysing it straight away.

2. E.g. The way puns and wordplay are used to make a light-hearted mood could be explained more to answer the 'how' part of the question. The second sentence should be more relevant to the question, as it focuses on characters rather than on the mood of the play.

Task: Your introduction and conclusion should both give a clear answer to the question. The introduction should include your main points, but no evidence. Your conclusion should summarise your argument and not include new points.

## Page 55: Writing About Context

1. a - 3, b - 1, c - 2

2. Contextual information: ... the difficulties that illegitimate children faced in the 16th century. / ... illegitimate children in the 16th century had no rights to their father's inheritance and had less power in society than their siblings.

3. You could have included context as the Explain or Develop part of the paragraph. The context you wrote about should be relevant to your Point and linked to the Example.

## Page 56: Linking Ideas and Paragraphs

1. E.g. Borachio is presented as manipulative. For example, in Act 5, Scene 1, he confesses that Don John "incensed" him to "slander" Hero, but in Act 1, Scene 3, it is Borachio who devises the plan to damage Hero's reputation. This shows that Borachio is willing to lie to make himself seem less guilty, which means it is easy for the audience to see him as one of the villains of the play.

2. You should have used the P.E.E.D. structure and included connecting words and phrases such as 'therefore' or 'which shows that' to link your ideas.

3. E.g. Moreover... / This idea is reinforced by...

## Page 57: Marking Answer Extracts

1. 4-5: The answer gives a thoughtful response, but there are some spelling errors. It examines how Shakespeare uses language, but doesn't analyse it closely enough for it to be a 6-7 answer. The answer doesn't include an exploration of contextual information.

## Page 58: Marking Answer Extracts

1. a) 8-9: E.g. "The Messenger emphasises... highlighting how few of his men died." — arguments supported with well-integrated, precise examples from the text
   "He is referred to as... shown to Don Pedro by other characters." — close and perceptive analysis of language

b) 6-7: E.g. "He vows to... that Leonato desires." — integrated, well-chosen examples
"This goes against... noble and respectable character." — exploration of the relationship between the text and its context

## Pages 59-60: Marking a Whole Answer

1. 8-9: E.g. The answer includes well-integrated, precise examples of how Shakespeare uses language, structure and form to convey ideas to the reader. There is a critical discussion of the relationship between the text and its social and historical context. The answer is well-written and uses highly relevant subject terminology.

## Page 61: Skills Focus — Writing Well

1. At the start of the play, Benedict's [Benedick's] disapproval of marrage [marriage] is used to create humour. He worried [worries] that he will not "see a bachelor of three-score' ["] again after Claudio confesses his desire to marry hero [Hero]. The phrase "of three score" means sixty years old. Most men in Shakespeares [Shakespeare's] time would have married by this age: [,] which makes Benedick's opinion seem slightly ridiculus [ridiculous].

2. a - 5, b - 2, c - 6, d - 3, e - 1, f - 4

## Page 62: Practice Questions

Your answers should have an introduction, several paragraphs developing different ideas and a conclusion. You may have covered some of the following points:

1. • In this extract, Shakespeare presents Beatrice as intelligent through her quick-wittedness. Immediately after the Messenger says Benedick is not in Beatrice's "books", Beatrice tells him she would "burn" her "study" if Benedick was in them. This shows that Beatrice is able to quickly think of a witty response to the Messenger's comment. However, rather than recognising her intelligence, an Elizabethan audience may have considered Beatrice's wit to be inappropriate, as they would have expected a woman to be quiet rather than outspoken and witty.

   • Shakespeare uses imagery of war to suggest that Beatrice is a match for Benedick in intelligence. Leonato says there is an ongoing "skirmish of wit" between the two of them, while Beatrice refers to one of their encounters as a "conflict". The words "skirmish" and "conflict" suggest that Beatrice and Benedick are engaged in a battle of their intellects. The fact that this battle has not been definitively won shows that Beatrice is Benedick's equal in intelligence. Later in the scene, Benedick says "I have done" and stops the argument, which could suggest that he is unable to think of another retort. This would imply that her intelligence is actually superior to his.

   • However, Beatrice does not always seem intelligent in the play. In one short soliloquy in Act 3, Scene 1, Beatrice goes from questioning Benedick's feelings, saying "Can this be true?", to believing in them and vowing to "requite" him. This sudden change reveals how quickly Beatrice accepts Hero and Ursula's claims, which makes her seem easy to fool. The fact that Beatrice has seemed intelligent and insightful until this point suggests that it is the thought of Benedick's love that has affected her ability to think clearly.

2. a) • Benedick's thoughts in this extract show how easily he can be fooled, which might amuse the audience. His first line of dialogue after the trick has been played on him is "This can be no trick." The dramatic irony here is funny for the audience, as they know that the opposite is true and Benedick's certainty is misplaced. At the end of the extract, Benedick claims he can "spy some marks of love" in Beatrice. This creates further humour for the audience, as the word "spy" suggests that Benedick thinks he has detected something that is hard to observe, when in reality there is nothing for him to see.

# Answers

- The audience might be suspicious of Benedick's sudden love for Beatrice in this extract. Benedick says he "must" return her love, despite suggesting earlier in the scene that a woman would have to be perfect and possess "all graces" at once to attract him. The fact that Benedick's attitude to love has changed so dramatically might make the audience doubt whether he truly loves Beatrice. However, later in the extract, he lists Beatrice's qualities, which match the "graces" he refers to earlier in the scene. This might convince the audience that his love is genuine.
- Benedick's positive response to criticism in this extract makes him more likeable to the audience. Benedick says understanding your own "detractions" is useful because you can "put them to mending". This shows he is willing to change to make himself a better person, which is a quality the audience is likely to admire. Benedick's willingness to abandon his pride in his status as a bachelor might have been particularly endearing to an Elizabethan audience, who might have seen Benedick's reluctance to marry as a character flaw.

b)
- Leonato's treatment of Hero in Act 4, Scene 1 might provoke sympathy for Hero. After Hero has fainted, Leonato says "Do not live, Hero" and "do not ope thine eyes" because he believes death is the best way to cover her "shame". Leonato's repeated use of the imperative "Do not" makes it seem as though he is ordering his daughter to die. This encourages the audience to pity Hero, as they know she is innocent and does not deserve to be treated so harshly. A modern audience might feel more sympathy for Hero, as they would expect Leonato to value Hero's life over honour, whereas an Elizabethan audience might agree with his motives for rejecting Hero.
- Hero deserves sympathy when Borachio and Don John plot against her in Act 2, Scene 2. Don John agrees to spoil Claudio and Hero's wedding because he is "sick in displeasure" to Claudio, even though the plot will also "undo Hero". This provokes sympathy for Hero, as it shows Don John does not care about destroying her if it means he can hurt Claudio. The fact that Hero's ruin is a secondary result of Don John's desire to hurt Claudio reflects her lack of power and importance in the play, which could increase the audience's sympathy for her.
- Shakespeare structures the play in a way that creates sympathy for Hero. In Act 3, Scene 4, Shakespeare shows Hero preparing for her wedding, but the audience has just learned in Act 3, Scene 3 that Claudio has sworn to "shame" Hero "before the whole congregation". Structuring the play in this way encourages the audience to feel sorry for Hero, as they know her preparations are pointless and she will be ruined at the wedding. The audience's sympathy for Hero is likely to increase at the start of Act 4 when Claudio says he has not come to the church to marry Hero, as this confirms that he does intend to shame her.

3.
- In this extract, Shakespeare presents Claudio as partly responsible for Hero's downfall. Leonato sarcastically refers to Claudio and Don Pedro as "a pair of honourable men" who have played a role in Hero's 'death'. Leonato's use of the adjective "honourable" is intended as a criticism, as it suggests that it was Claudio and Don Pedro's desire to protect their own honour that led to Hero's wrongful shaming. Leonato's attitude suggests to the audience that Claudio will not be instantly forgiven for his actions, which reflects his role as a traditional romantic hero who must prove that they have atoned for their mistakes before achieving happiness.
- Claudio is shown to be insincere in this extract. Claudio tells Leonato to "Impose" any "penance" on him for his treatment of Hero, but then claims "sinned I not / But in mistaking". A "penance" is a punishment that is intended to express remorse. Claudio's desire to do penance implies that he wants to make amends, but his claim that his only sin was making a mistake suggests that he believes his actions were justified. This makes his remorse seem insincere, as it

shows that he is not fully convinced that he deserves to be punished. Claudio's insincerity might cause the audience to question whether Leonato should forgive him, as it encourages them to view Claudio as untrustworthy.
- Elsewhere in the play, Claudio is presented as a traditional courtly lover through his language. Claudio often uses poetic language, such as in Act 2, Scene 1 when he uses a metaphor to describe "beauty" as a "witch" that can make a person's loyalty disappear. In Elizabethan England, poetry was traditionally associated with courtly love, so Claudio's use of poetic language highlights his status as a courtly lover to the audience. This impression is reinforced by the fact that, throughout the play, Claudio often speaks in blank verse, while other characters mainly speak in prose.

4. a)
- Shakespeare uses Hero's language to present her as confident in this extract. Hero uses a series of imperatives when explaining Margaret's role in the deception, such as "run thee", "tell her" and "Say that". This makes Hero sound authoritative and shows she has absolute confidence in the orders she is giving. Hero's confidence reflects the strict hierarchy of 16th-century society, where noblewomen like Hero had power over those with lower social status.
- The structure of the dialogue in this extract makes Hero seem confident. Hero speaks extensively in two long sections of dialogue that are only broken up by Margaret's short line acknowledging Hero's orders. Hero's ability to speak fluently at length suggests that she knows what she wants to say and feels comfortable being in charge of executing the trick. Hero's lengthy speech in this scene contrasts with her near silence in Act 1, Scene 1 when she is surrounded by men, which suggests she is less confident in situations where she has limited power.
- Hero's belief that the trick will fool Beatrice makes her seem confident. She says that their trick will create "little Cupid's crafty arrow". Hero's allusion to Cupid's "arrow" likens the effects of their trick to Cupid's mythological power of making people fall in love, while the word "crafty" suggests that the trick is too clever to be detected. This highlights Hero's conviction that Beatrice will be caught out by their trap. The fact that Hero associates herself with a god in this scene might make her seem overconfident to the audience, as her skills of manipulation have not yet been proven.

b)
- As in many of Shakespeare's comedies, a secret scheme is used to cause trouble for the main characters. In Act 1, Scene 2, the audience is told that Don John wants to cause "mischief". This leads him to deceive Don Pedro and Claudio and eventually results in Hero being rejected at the wedding, so this secret scheme introduces more tragic elements to the plot than would appear in a typical Shakespearean comedy. However, Shakespeare also uses a secret scheme to resolve the tragic parts of the plot, as Leonato's plan to disguise Hero as her 'cousin' leads to her and Claudio being reunited.
- Some secret schemes in the play show that deception can have positive results. In Act 3, Scene 1, Hero and Ursula's trick makes Beatrice realise that she wants to "bind" herself to Benedick "in a holy band". Beatrice's newfound willingness to consider marriage would have been seen as a positive consequence by an Elizabethan audience, who would have expected women like her to marry. The word "bind" has both positive and negative associations, as it can suggest either closeness or being restrained. This might make the audience question whether marriage is a positive result for Beatrice.
- Secret schemes serve a key role in developing the plot of the play. In Act 1, Scene 1, Don Pedro promises to "disguise" himself as Claudio and woo Hero on his behalf. This scheme sets the main plot of the play into motion as it leads to Leonato agreeing that Claudio and Hero can marry. By ending the first scene of the play with two of the main characters planning a secret scheme, Shakespeare hints to the audience that deception and trickery will be important in the rest of the play.

# The Characters from 'Much Ado About Nothing'

After all those questions, you should be a *Much Ado About Nothing* maestro. Time to reward yourself with a little light relief. Get comfy and feast your eyes on *Much Ado About Nothing — The Cartoon*...

# William Shakespeare's 'Much Ado About Nothing'

ETWMA41